BOXING THE BLUES
AWAY

Amy Brenneman

Stanton&
Samuel

Dedication

To my amazing husband Scott, who stood by my side during The Dark Times, and to my wonderful children, Maverick and Macie Jayne, who make every day worth living to the fullest. I love you with all of my heart and more.

And for all the women who have suffered from postpartum depression and anyone who has experienced mental illness in their lives, this is for you. Please remember to keep hope alive. Your health and happiness are worth fighting for.

Contents

Roy Jones Jr. and Amy Brenneman

Foreword

Like many professional athletes, during my time as a world boxing champion, when out in public—at the airport, in a shopping mall, or in a restaurant—I was frequently recognized. When people would come right up to me, I always tried to be engaging because that's my nature. But most of the time, you would just see them either stare and excitedly point and whisper to someone else, or you would get the occasional shout-out from a true fan: "Yo, Roy Jones Jr.! What up?"

It was a regular and daily occurrence in my life and I never really minded it, even though it always surprised me how many people knew who I was, especially since growing up and living in Pensacola, Florida, where I was treated like a regular neighbor, or a friend, or "that's Roy Jones Sr.'s boy"—stuff like that. Nothing special other than folks congratulating me on my success in the boxing ring.

So, it was always a little amusing and even refreshing when I would meet someone who either vaguely had heard of me or had no idea who I was.

Because those are the people who have no pretense or bias of who you are. They simply size you up based on an introduction and initial impression.

Such was the case when I met Amy Brenneman. My good friend and publicist Greg Fritz introduced us at his home in Manhattan Beach, California. Their families were close, and Amy and Greg grew up in the same hometown. It was plainly obvious that Amy had no clue who I was. She was cordial, but then became a little giddy and even nervous, as Greg methodically went through my entire boxing resume to try to draw some shred of recognition or emotional response from her. While Greg grew more exasperated, I became more entertained by the whole scene. It was like something out of a charade or "Who Am I?" game.

At this point, poor Amy I think was becoming a little overwhelmed, so that's when I stepped in and asked her if she would like to learn a few boxing moves. She reticently accepted my offer. While she was slim, healthy, and athletic, she was not a natural boxer, so we spent the next hour going through some basic moves. The more she learned, the more excited and enthralled she became. She asked questions and eagerly shadowed every move I made. As Amy gained new confidence and levels of achievement, she would hop around and squealed with joy in her newfound agility and coordination.

Overall, that first meeting was a fun evening. Since I was staying at Greg's house at the time, we all got together several times after that, and I really enjoyed Amy's company, her genuine enthusiasm, inquisitiveness, and bubbly personality. She always seemed so upbeat and buoyant as she displayed a true passion for life and adventure. At least that is what I thought. And that is what I saw on the surface.

During that first chance meeting and years later into our friendship, I was completely unaware that Amy was suffering internally from a dark, haunting, and relentless state of depression. You would never know she was silently struggling to stay afloat, desperately staving off a twisting mental and emotional spiral that was pulling her into a bottomless hole that she could see no way out of.

That's the difference between an invisible, demonic, and perpetual psychological state of despair versus those who show obvious physical ailments or disabilities. It was easy for me to befriend and offer kind words of encouragement to people I met with visible disabilities, injuries, ailments, and conditions. But how do you identify, and then treat, those who are hurting and dealing with a state of depression on the inside and camouflaging it so well?

Fortunately for Amy and me, just being myself somehow ignited a slow but deliberate healing process that eventually brought her back from the precipice of hopelessness and despair. In this case, it was simply an act of friendship and sharing an athletic ability that I consider a gift from God, with someone desperately looking for a sign or hand to pull them from the cavernous, lonely abyss. And the amazing part of this story is how easy and effortless it was for me to provide that lifeline she needed. The focus, purpose, and energy to realize life is worth living. As I mentioned before, I never saw evidence or signs in Amy of severe depression and suicidal tendencies.

All I did was show her a few boxing moves. And while a simple introduction eventually became a strong friendship for Amy and me, she goes on to describe it all in her book as a healing process—an eventual resurrection that offers others afflicted with depression and lost hope a complete turnaround in their lives as well. But they need to seek it out by channeling their own unleashed passions and connect those undiscovered enthusiasms through primarily family and friends, or a new acquaintance that blossoms into a trusted friendship, as pillars of support.

No one can lift themselves from the jagged, frenzied suicidal path on their own. In her book, Amy provides you with the signposts you need to follow to find reason, purpose, and verve in living a satisfying life. By telling her story, she hopes to inspire others who are living in fear, anxiety, and uncertainty by saying, "You are not alone, and help is available to you if you just look for it."

—Roy Jones Jr.

Introduction

DOWN BUT NOT OUT

I t was February 2, Groundhog Day. I was lying in bed, unable to sleep as usual, staring at the clock, and watching the time go by. As I lie awake, tossing and turning, all I could do was think about the movie *Groundhog Day* and sadly come to terms with how closely my life resembled that film. From the moment I woke up until the time I went to bed, the tedious, mundane routine of my life constantly remained the same. Each day seemed to repeat itself and blend into one another. It didn't matter how bright and sunny it was outside, it was always going to be a cold, dark, gloomy day in my mind. I felt the same frustration as Phil Connors did in that film as he woke up each morning to the sound of the blaring alarm clock and dreaded arising from his bed, only to relive the same day over and over again. Sadly, I realized my life was not much different. Day after day, things rarely changed. My future was beginning to look quite bleak and grim, like those winter days that would never end.

It had been a long time, months in fact, where I no longer felt hope or the light of a new day. Just as in the movie, I could predict the outcome of every moment throughout each day. Things rarely changed in my somber world. Any joy I may have once felt was completely stripped away. Like Phil Connors, I felt trapped with no means of escape. The difference was, it wasn't a blizzard that was keeping me locked up. Instead, I was being held back by my own oppressive mind.

My long, restless, sleepless night had finally come to an end as I watched the sun rise up over the hills from my bedroom window. I folded back my covers, lethargically got out of bed, glanced in the mirror at my dark, droopy eyes, and slowly but surely made my way down the stairs. I brewed a cup of coffee, then painfully walked over to the same black comfy but weathered, leather couch I would inhabit most every day. After wrapping myself up in my old, tattered, but cozy blanket, I turned on the TV and eventually found the news station. Somewhat curious to know, I checked to see what the famous groundhog Punxsutawney Phil had predicted for our weather that year, though, it didn't really matter what the outcome was going to be. Even if the groundhog had predicted the coming of an early spring, it still would have remained a gray, cloudy, cold winter in my head. Pathetic, I know. It was not how I ever imagined I would be living my life, nor was I proud of how I felt inside.

Just once, I had hoped to wake up energized and enthusiastic about taking on the day. Sadly, but not surprisingly, it never happened. I was overwhelmingly let down and became tired, weak, anxious, irritable, and depressed. I was mentally and physically exhausted. A change was desperately needed as I was literally losing my appetite for life.

At 5'4" and a mere 88 pounds, I was withering away to nothing and looked noticeably unhealthy. I could no longer function that way. I needed help, but I wasn't sure where to go or who to turn to as I had tried so many unsuccessful modalities before.

Based on my appearance alone, it may have looked like I had an eating disorder, but that was surely not the case. Nor had I ever been addicted to drugs or alcohol. Cancer was not the culprit this time either.

What I had was a sickness many others have also endured.

Like millions of people, I, too, had been suffering from depression. However, my type of depression was something that was not well recognized or perhaps, I should say, well received at the time. Though I have suffered from anxiety and depression most of my life, this one was unique and very grim. The type of depression I was suffering from this time around was called "postpartum depression" (PPD). It was the kind of deep, dark, desolate feeling some women experience after having a baby.

PPD had affected millions of mothers and had been going untreated or was misunderstood for years. Like most types of depression, it could range anywhere from mild to moderate or, in certain cases, severe. Some women would feel like, or actually go through with, hurting their babies. Others could potentially become suicidal. The most severe cases were ones in which the mother actually killed her own child or children. Perhaps a majority of those mothers and babies could have been saved had we only used the tools and know-how to help them.

Though I battled with mild to moderate depression before, this was not something to take lightly. PPD was a serious illness that dramatically affected my family and almost cost me my life. Not only was I losing weight and becoming extremely unhealthy, but with each day that passed, I was losing a piece of myself. The best parts of my personality and charismatic nature had been hidden deep down and were made worse coupled with the tragedies of my past. Looking in the mirror, I hardly recognized myself anymore. My eyes were still their usual olive-green color, yet they seemed deadened and hollow inside. Becoming quite transparent was the fact I felt listless and disheartened, powerless and ashamed. There was much more to me than the pathetic, morose-looking figure that stood before me in the mirror.

I was severely damaged and dangerously depressed. Fear and anxiety were the culprits that had been beating me up inside: fear of not being a good enough wife or mother; fear of disappointing the people I loved; fear that I would never be strong enough to overcome the challenges I faced. Lastly, it was the fear of all things I had endured in my past that continued to haunt me. Those feelings of fear and unworthiness wore me down to the point where I could have "accidently" taken my own life.

Even though I had dealt with depression before, it had finally reached excessive heights. The thought of suicide chills me to the bones and would never normally enter my mind, but I was there living it, dreaming it—I'm not sure which. But like a movie, I watched it happen. It was a place I hadn't gone before and had zero plans to return. Frankly, that meant making a significant change in the way I was living—or not living—my life.

I was down but not out. It was almost as if I could hear the referee counting. Lying there on the couch, I faintly heard in my mind, *What are you going to do about your life?* Then it was if the countdown began—ten, nine, eight, seven, six, five. Before the voice in my head got to "one," it hit me (pun intended), that very February 2, Groundhog Day, what it was I needed to do to change my life for good. I sat up on my couch (still pathetically cocooned in my blanket) and thought about what I had done in the past that helped whenever I was feeling depressed or upset. I wracked my brain over what I could possibly do to get better when so many attempts at different healing strategies had failed me before. I thought I had tried everything. I went to counseling and saw a psychiatrist, I practiced Eye Movement Desensitization and Reprocessing (EMDR), I worked on Neuro-Linguistic Programming (NLP), I practiced bilateral tapping, I got massages, tested out yoga, and even tried hypnotherapy.

While I don't want to say those modalities weren't helpful, because they did play their part in minor healing, they just weren't enough to get me through the darkest times. After a bit of deep thought, it finally hit me. I quickly uncurled myself from the blanket I had practically lived in for the past year, and jetted up the stairs to my bedroom. Pulling a stool into my closet, I reached up high and grabbed the big, white cardboard box on the top shelf labeled "Amy's Treasures." The words were written in bright, colorful rainbow stickers, but the box itself had been a tad worn. I stepped back down off the stool and walked over to my bed. Lifting the top, I was excited to see the "treasures" that had been hidden away for so long. As I peered inside and lifted out some of my most memorable items, I found what I was searching for. There they were, good as new—the bright, red boxing gloves that had been signed and given to me by a special friend and boxing legend, Roy Jones Jr.

A gigantic smile spread across my face as I realized there was possibly a tinge of hope. *This could be the answer I'm looking for*, I thought. I reached into the box and carefully pulled the boxing gloves out. Excitedly, I slipped them over my tiny hands. Immediately attracted to the brilliant, red color, I began to feel joy and a slight bit of inspiration from trying them on again. I looked in the full-length mirror at myself standing there with those beautiful red gloves on. It helped me see myself in a new light. At that moment, I had an epiphany. I realized that to change my life, let go of my fears, and get out of this horrific, depressing slump I had been in—clearly and simply—I needed to become a fighter. I had to learn to become a fighter in all aspects of my life. Once I recognized the potential I had inside, my life began to change. That marked the day I began "boxing the blues away."

Round 1

ROY JONES JR. IS IN MY CORNER

The first day I met Roy Jones Jr. is still very clear and vivid in my mind. My close family friend Greg had let me know Roy and his buddy Derrick Gainer (nicknamed Smoke) were coming to his house to work on some promotional items. Greg was Roy Jones Jr.'s public relations and media manager at the time. He invited me over to meet the guys and hang out for a bit. It sounded good to me, so I immediately checked my calendar. Fortunately, I didn't have any clients on the books that day. I figured it sounded like a pretty cool thing to do, so why the heck not? I packed up a few things I needed for the drive and headed to Manhattan Beach near L.A., where Greg was currently living. Hopping into my little two-seater, red, Honda CRX, off I went to meet some guys who just happened to be famous boxers.

It's actually quite a funny story because I really didn't know who Roy Jones Jr. was back then. Plus, I was used to being around famous athletes since I had been working with many of them already. I wasn't someone who would get starstruck easily. However, little did I know this would be the man who made one of the biggest impacts on my life, and Greg as well since this wouldn't have happened without him.

Even though I was a huge sports lover, I was not a fan of boxing at all. In fact, when I heard my dad talk about how Greg was a public relations manager for this famous guy, I thought he was talking about a basketball player. Apparently, Roy loved to play basketball as well. Supposedly, he was an incredible player. So, my dad would just talk about how good he was at basketball. I didn't realize boxing was Roy's main sport until later.

Growing up I loved every single sport except for the ones that involved fighting. If I wasn't playing different sports with the neighborhood kids out in the street or in our backyard, some type of professional or college sport was always on the TV. The times when it was boxing night, I just wanted to run away or at least go to another room where I didn't have to hear or see anything.

My dad and brothers had a field day watching the hard punches thrown and yelling at the top of their lungs when someone landed a good hit. Being super sensitive to noise, it drove me nuts to hear their loud shouting and screaming at the TV. Occasionally, I would sit in the living room with them when a match was on, but I had to look the other way or cover my eyes with my hands when I saw the blood and sweat fly off the fighters' bodies. It literally made my stomach turn. I just couldn't understand why anyone would want to be in such an icky profession.

My dad and brothers watched all the great fighters. There was no real way to avoid the fights because I mostly did whatever my family was doing. We saw Muhammad Ali, Floyd Mayweather, George Foreman, Sugar Ray Leonard, Evander Holyfield, Oscar De La Hoya, Manny Pacquiao, Mike Tyson, and of course the legendary Rocky Balboa as well as many others. I even ran into Lennox Lewis at a dance club in Newport Beach one night. He was very charming and nice to the fans around him. That was the first experience I had with a famous boxer who seemed to be a nice, friendly person. I don't know why the thought stumped me so much. I guess I felt that to be a good fighter, you must be really tough and mean all the time. Needless to say, I really didn't know much about boxers.

I will admit once the major fight came out where Mike Tyson bit off Evander Holyfield's ear, I was done with boxing for good. My family and I watched it in real time, and I had never been subjected to something so incredibly disturbing as that. My days of watching boxing were *over*—that was until the day I met Roy Jones Jr.

My little, red car had made the drive to Manhattan Beach, and I finally pulled up in front of Greg's house. As I started to walk up the steps, my buddy opened up the door to greet me and invited me inside. There, in the kitchen, were two of Greg's boxing buddies. He first introduced me to Roy who smiled, shook my hand and said, "Very nice to meet you." Then Roy introduced me to his pal, Smoke, who was a featherweight fighter.

They were both standing in the kitchen going through boxes of gloves and had several professional pictures to sign. Roy immediately took out one of his pictures and signed it, "To Amy, the sweet cutie of L.A." I'm sure I must have blushed a bit when he handed it to me. Then he also asked if I would like a pair of signed boxing gloves. Well, of course you don't say no to that, so I was quite pleased to receive my first and only pair of real boxing gloves. Better yet, they were signed by one of the best boxers in the world.

We all hung out at Greg's house for a little bit. To get things started, Roy thought it would be fun to do some boxing training with me, probably because I asked him if he would, or perhaps I might have mouthed off telling him I could kick his butt. That sounds a tad more like me. Whatever the case was, I started having a fun little lesson with him. Of course, I didn't let Roy know my disgust over the sport at the time because he was really sweet and kind of cute too. I figured I could let those old thoughts go as I was easily persuaded by his smile and charm.

Roy and I walked into the front room where we had more space to move around. Then he started having me practice some punches with the boxing gloves on. He told me to punch him as hard as I could in the stomach. Being the nice girl I was, his request made me slightly uncomfortable. I said, "But I don't want to hurt you." I don't think I've heard anyone laugh so hard. He just thought it was the funniest thing for me to be afraid of hurting him, or more so because I thought I could hurt him.

After the laughter settled, Roy demanded I punch him as hard as I could. Finally, I obliged and hit Roy in the stomach with all the strength that my tiny, little hand could muster. He let out a slight giggle and said, "Is that all you got? Come on, hit me! Use some fire!" So, I kept punching him over and over as hard as possible. His stomach was like a solid brick wall I could not possibly put a dent in. I tried with all my might, but it must have felt like a little butterfly wing or a soft flower petal brushing up against his skin. In the end, my hand ended up getting sore, not him. Therefore, we moved onto a different type of training.

The next thing Roy taught me was how to do the "jab, jab, cross." It became my most favorite move of all time. I had so much fun with it. Roy was showing me how to take two baby steps forward with my left foot first, while also jabbing with my left hand. I must admit my little steps and jabs were pathetic. He kept laughing at my terrible form and technique. I had to agree it was definitely tease-worthy. Yes, I was very much out of my league. Roy was a good coach, though, and would redirect me and make me practice until I got it right (or at least until it was good enough for a rookie).

Eventually, I had made decent enough progress with my jabs so we could move on to the right cross. Thank goodness I got to use my dominant hand for this, which felt a hell of a lot better. Dancing around, jabbing, and crossing, with a hard, right punch while trying to hit Roy was one of the highlights of my day. For a while, we just practiced that: jab, jab, cross—jab, jab, cross. I was having a blast! Then we did some bob and weave techniques which were also loads of fun. The practicing made me laugh pretty hard. I just felt like dancing around. Who knew that fighting could be so much fun and entertaining? Was I beginning to have a mind shift about the sport I had previously despised so much? It certainly didn't hurt to have a fit, extremely muscular, funny, professional boxer around who could persuade me to alter my original way of thinking. I may have been turning over a new leaf after all. How could I not with someone like Roy Jones Jr. in my corner?

Along with working on public relations, Roy was also in Los Angeles because he was invited to be a guest star on the acclaimed sitcom *Married with Children*. My friend Greg knew I had met a couple of celebrities from that show through my hockey player friends. They were on the Anaheim Mighty Ducks team. Greg thought I would enjoy going along to the taping of the show with him and the other guys, so he invited me to be their guest. Greg was right. I was thrilled to be invited and accepted the invitation without reservation.

When we were talking about *Married with Children*, Greg made a remark in front of Roy about how I should go because I was "friends" with those guys. Giggling with a bit of shyness and embarrassment, I felt the need to set the record straight. They weren't exactly friends of mine, I admitted. I was a sports massage therapist during the time and had clients in the National Hockey League (NHL). I preferred working with athletes, mainly because I was an athlete myself, and I felt it was easier to set boundaries with them. My work was not conducted in a dark and secretive environment. What I'm trying to say is I made it very clear there would be a happy ending without a "happy ending," if you catch my drift. I wanted to be professional in the sports world and took my career seriously. For the most part, I worked with a few of the Anaheim Mighty Ducks and Los Angeles Kings players. There were a few other NHL players I knew from various teams who would also call me when they were coming to town.

One of my friends on the Mighty Ducks team, Sean Hill, was good buddies with Ted McGinley who was an actor on *Married with Children.* Personally, I had been more familiar with Ted McGinley when he was staring on the hit TV series *Happy Days* as Roger and as a photographer on the popular show *The Love Boat*, though I guess admitting that may age me.

Actually, a funny thing happened with regards to Ted McGinley before Sean formally introduced us. My friend Cindy and I went to a celebrity hockey game at what was then called the "Anaheim Pond." After the hockey event was over, there was a special party for the celebrities, hockey players, and their guests. Cindy and I had just walked through the hallway and were heading toward the elevators. We were standing by the elevator, waiting for it to come back down, when suddenly the glass doors opened behind us, and in walked our favorite L. A. Kings hockey player, Shawn McEachern. He was followed by, none other than, Ted McGinley.

At first, we didn't even realize it was Ted McGinley because we were freaking out over the fact that my best friend's biggest crush was walking right toward us. Our faces must have turned bright red. We quickly got out a camera and excitedly asked the other nice gentleman with Shawn McEachern if he would please take our picture with him. Boy, did we ask the right guy. As it turned out, he was a professional photographer from *The Love Boat*! He must have had some practice taking photos because the picture could not have turned out any better. But it wasn't until Ted smiled and nicely handed me back my camera that it hit me who he was. Cindy and I looked at each other and grinned. By then, we were feeling sort of embarrassed about making a big scene over Shawn. I was bummed we didn't get a picture with Mr. "Handsome" McGinley too. It was a missed opportunity for sure, or so we thought at the time.

After we caught our breath and calmed down a bit, we headed upstairs to the party. There were so many famous celebrities in the beautifully decorated room. As we left the elevator and started walking forward, the first person we came into contact with was the late Alan Thicke. He was extraordinarily friendly and made eye contact, saying hello to us with a happy grin as he walked by. Next, I was elated to see Michelle Pfeiffer sitting down at a round table with white, satin linen, and illuminating candles. She looked like an absolute goddess, who never seems to age. I'm not sure if it's Hollywood, money, or just good genes, but Michelle Pfeiffer always looks fantastic.

Though there were other highly famous celebrities at the party who I'm sure would have been fun to meet, we preferred to spend our time with the players from the Mighty Ducks hockey team and some of their friends from Boston who came along to visit. We hung out with the Boston crowd for quite some time. The boys were there to visit Bob Corkum. We met Bob's brother and a couple of his friends. I don't know if it was their teasing and smart-aleck behavior, their humorous personalities, or just the fun accents which kept us around. Whatever it was became something special because my best friend Cindy met her future husband that night. Who would have guessed it? Now married for over 20 years, those silly kids are currently living just outside the Boston area with three beautiful daughters. They live in the same town one of my favorite comedy actors, John Cena, grew up. When I was visiting Cindy in Massachusetts, I got to see his family's gorgeous mansion up on the hill from a distance. Admittedly, I wasn't a fan of John Cena's when he was a wrestler (again, the sweat and blood did not entice me, nor did the screaming and obnoxious yelling), but as an actor I think he is absolutely hilarious. His facial expressions and timing are so good, I have to give him props. Based on his movie characters, he seems like a very funny man with a naughty sense of humor—the kind I love.

Back at the celebrity hockey party, we continued to stay to the end of the night. When the party was finally closing down, we said goodbye to the Boston boys, headed down the elevators, and continued to hang out with several of our hockey player friends. The guys on the team were hilarious and extremely entertaining to be around. This was back in the day when the Anaheim Mighty Ducks team was brand new. Now they are just called the "Ducks," thank goodness. That baby Disney name needed to go. It didn't belong associated with tough men who were getting in fights and checking each other against the boards.

As far as hockey teams went, I really didn't discriminate. I grew up watching the Los Angeles Kings with Cindy before the Ducks team was even formed. The older group of Kings players were my favorite. My friend Cheryl, Cindy, and I would typically go to Harry O's in Manhattan Beach after the Kings games and hang out with many of the players. We got to know them pretty well since I was working with a few of them. We would get invited to their parties and end of the season events. We even got to meet the legendary Wayne Gretzky at one of the parties held at Rob Blake's house. Though most of them were super cool guys, I will never forget Rob's kindness and generosity. As huge a star as he was and still is in the hockey world, he was one of the most genuine and humble professional hockey players I knew. Even though these were all nice guys, Roy Jones

Jr. still takes the cake for all-time favorite athletes, of course.

Before I move on, I must mention my talented brother-in-law since I have been discussing favorite professional athletes. My sister Kara married Paul McDonnell, a professional soccer player who grew up in Newcastle, England. Paul began his career playing soccer in the U.K. for Sunderland. Then he transferred to the U.S. and played for both the Los Angeles Galaxy team and the Anaheim Splash indoor soccer league. I've been told that he was a pretty decent football (soccer in the U.K.) player. The deejay I had at my wedding happened to be from England and recognized Paul from his professional soccer days over there. That was a bit surprising and cool at the same time. Another surprise was Paul telling me he hung out with Sean Hill and other hockey players I was friends with during the same time. Paul is definitely a fun brother-in-law to have around. He keeps the parties lively and is quite an entertaining bloke.

Back to how I met the *Married with Children* stars, I was attending one of the Ducks games. After the hockey game had ended, Sean introduced me to one of his buddies who just so happened to be Ted McGinley. As Sean was formally introducing us, I giggled to myself, politely shook Ted's hand, and said, "Hello, nice to meet you." I acted as if it was the first time I had ever seen him. I thought it would sound silly to say, "Oh hey, don't you remember me? We've already met. I asked you to take a picture of my friend and I with Shawn McEachern that night at the celebrity hockey game." Surely, I did not expect him to remember me and, though it was the truth, it would have sounded lame. I admit I can be a huge nerd, but I at least have a little sense at times. Instead, I just politely greeted him and moved on.

On a separate evening, after a Ducks game, we all went out to a restaurant and bar called The Catch. One of my good friends Cheryl, who I mentioned earlier, was a bartender there, so I loved to go and hang out with her after the games. It was a happening place whenever the Ducks or Anaheim Angels had a game in town. One of my girlfriends and I had been sitting at a little table on the side of the bar when Ted walked over and said hello. He introduced us to his friend David Faustino, who played Bud Bundy on *Married with Children*, and asked if he could join us at the table. We said yes, of course, then Ted went to the bar to get some drinks. It was David's birthday that night. He was very nice, and my friend and I kept a light conversation going with him for a while. Though I must tell you how hard it was to keep a straight face and not call him "Bud." It took some real inner strength and concentration, but I did it—I was able to make it through the night without snickering and accidently calling him Bud Bundy. All in all, he was actually a very nice guy to talk to.

And that is how I came to know Ted McGinley (Jefferson D'Arcy) and David Faustino (Bud Bundy) from the show *Married with Children*.

So, here we were again at Greg's house getting ready to leave and drive to the set of *Married with Children*. Roy had an earlier call time, so Greg and I met him over at the set a little later. We found Roy in his dressing room when we got there and were told there were a couple other big-name sports stars who would be joining him on set. In addition to the famous boxer Roy Jones Jr. was the All-Star professional baseball and football player Bo Jackson. Larry Brown, a

Dallas Cowboys and Oakland Raiders football player who was named MVP of Super Bowl XXX, was there as well. Those were some pretty major sports celebrities to all be in the same room together. Being a big sports fan myself, I'd say it was a pretty incredible day. Not only did I get to meet Mr. Bo Jackson, but word was spreading that I was a sports massage therapist. So, when he came into Roy's dressing room, he asked if I could help him out. Bo said he was having some pains, and I was happy to try and help him. No way could I turn him down, even though I was intimidated by how large and muscular he was. He was so tall I couldn't even reach his shoulders if I stood on my tippy toes, so I asked him to please sit in a chair. It wasn't much, but I did what I could to try to take some of his pain away. As big and intimidating as he looked, he ended up being just a giant, sweet, teddy bear. He was very grateful and thanked me kindly for helping him.

Next, I walked out of Roy's dressing room to take a little walk around with Greg and explore the set. The first person we ran into was Ted McGinley. Since he already knew me from his hockey buddy, we said hello, and I introduced him to Greg. Then, my being a massage therapist came up again. Ted said, "Amy, you know who could really use a massage right now? Ed O'Neil." Not a moment later, the star of the show, Ed O'Neil, walked up and Ted introduced me to him. Mr. O'Neil opened his eyes wide when he heard the word "massage."

It didn't happen often, but I have to admit I did become a little starstruck by this man. There, standing in front of me, shaking my hand was one of my most beloved characters of all time—it was "Mr. Al Bundy" himself. He was smiling and looking at me with the most magnificent piercing blue eyes. I always viewed Ed O'Neil like you see him on the television screen with pale looking skin, a flabby body, a silly grin on his face, sitting down, slumped over with one hand down his pants, saying something to Peg or his kids in a moody, whiny voice. This was not the same guy. Not even close. The man standing in front of me was tall and fit, kind but also serious. The talks I had with him showed his intellect was much higher than I ever imagined for someone who played such a silly character. I'm pretty sure I was the one who sounded like an idiot when Ed told me he had been having some nagging back pain and wondered if I could help fix it. "Uh, uh, uh, yes of course I would be happy to, um, help you with your mack plane, I mean back pain, Mr. O'Neil," I said. At least, that's what I thought I must have sounded like. Hopefully I held it together better than that, but I was pretty nervous.

Before he said goodbye and went back to his dressing room, Ed made sure to politely let Greg and I know we were invited to stay for lunch with everyone. He was such an impressive man. One of my fondest memories was definitely getting to work with Ed O'Neil. He was a true stand-up kind of guy, and I was baffled at how different he was in person from his character on screen. Al Bundy and Ed O'Neil were both pretty remarkable men. One just happened to be a lot goofier than the other.

Next, it was time for lunch. We all walked over to the restaurant at the studio where there was a buffet of all kinds of unique and delicious foods to eat. There were plenty of healthy varieties (most likely for the actors who needed to stay fit), but I headed straight for the pasta, bread, and desserts. There were infinite and wonderous chocolate masterpieces I could not pass up either. I definitely wasn't interested in being a model. Instead, I dove right in and had myself quite the feast. Best news was I got to eat anything I wanted for free. It was nice to have a small taste of what it must feel like to be a celebrity and receive a little special treatment. I also enjoyed people watching as various actors from other studios came in to have lunch as well.

After we had plenty to eat and our bellies were full, we went back and hung out at the set. We visited David Faustino in his dressing room for a little bit before heading back to spend the rest of the time with Roy. It was almost showtime, and the actors were getting ready to perform in front of a live audience. Greg and I were soon escorted to our seats on the bleachers where we would be viewing the show with the rest of the audience.

Married with Children was about to begin with the added guest stars Roy Jones Jr., Bo Jackson, and Larry Brown. It was a brilliantly funny performance by all. One of the most memorable moments was when Roy Jones Jr. asked Marcy D'Arcy, "Excuse me, aren't you Bruce Jenner?" (Ironically, this was several years before Bruce Jenner's transformation.) Roy's question was laugh-out-loud funny, and Marcy's crazy reaction was comical too. The whole show was a ton of fun to watch in person. Getting to see the mistakes and bloopers when the actors messed up their lines was also quite entertaining.

After the show had wrapped, the entire cast and crew went out on stage to take pictures. I believe this was their last or next to last show of the season. Peg Bundy, played by Katey Sagal, sadly was not there. It was a slight bummer because I would have loved to have seen her in person. I think she is an amazing actress. The cast and crew who were at the set that day took nice photos and then some extremely silly pictures as well. When they were finished, the guests of the show were allowed to go on stage and take some pictures of their own. I was so excited to go up and sit on the old, gold couch displayed in practically every episode of the show. Roy and I had fun shooting a few silly pictures of our own. And I finally got my very own chance to get a picture with Ted McGinley since I had missed the opportunity on that night so long ago. At the set, I was not too embarrassed to ask and finally felt happy and fulfilled. The picture, taken by someone else, didn't hold up to the one he photographed for us. He might have truly been a real professional photographer after all.

When we were finally getting ready to leave the set, Greg asked me if I would drive Roy back to his house because he was going to take Smoke. I can't quite remember what exactly Roy and I talked about. However, I can recall laughing so hard my stomach hurt from whatever the conversation was. Never had I thought a boxer could be so funny and charismatic. My original thoughts and views were skewed. I'm completely embarrassed to admit I figured boxers would be really dumb from getting hit in the head too many times. What a jerk I was to be so shallow and ignorant. I knew *nothing* about boxers. Besides, who was I to talk? I personally have had four concussions from stupid accidents. Turns out, I was wrong in my thinking. Boxers are some of the fittest and best athletes in the world, and many are quite intelligent as well.

Beyond his boxing career, Roy also obtained a college degree and has all kinds of other talents. Remember, he is also a professional basketball player (wink). Actually, he probably could have been. He is also a pretty decent hip-hop artist. I have heard him rap a number of times. In spite of my original thoughts, I am glad I learned a lesson and was humbled. It helped me become aware not to stereotype or pass judgment on others. It would be wonderful if all people would do the same. At least I am able to admit my mistakes and learn from them.

After a fun-filled car ride, we finally arrived back at Greg's. Since it was getting fairly late, I got ready to make the long drive back to my own house. I located the picture and boxing gloves Roy had signed for me, gathered the rest of my belongings, and made my way toward the door. Then I hugged Smoke, Greg, and Roy and thanked each one of them for the incredible time I had with all of them. Those were some amazing memories I am grateful to have made and will definitely never forget, especially since those times are what initially started my interactions with Roy. It amazes me to think back to that day and realize how my life has changed for the better because of it.

Round 2

RINGSIDE SEAT

The next time I met up with Roy Jones Jr. was at his boxing match in Las Vegas, Nevada, at one of the major casinos, I believe the MGM Grand. My friend Cheryl and I were invited to attend. It wasn't just Roy fighting that night, although his match was the main event. There were several other boxing matches scheduled to go on before his.

One of the most fascinating fights of the evening besides Roy's was, interestingly enough, a girl fight. I remember that Christy Martin, an American world champion, was one of the women fighting that night. Her opponent was an exceptional fighter as well, however, she couldn't hold up to the sheer strength and athletic talent of Christy Martin.

Before any of the fights for the evening began, I was coming down the elevator alone when the doors opened, and in stepped the famous fighter of the night—Christy Martin herself. To say I was a bit uncomfortable was an understatement. That woman looked fierce, and you could just feel the intense energy coming off her. Making eye contact, I gave her the stupidest, sheepish grin while all the time thinking, *One wrong move and this woman could seriously knock the crap out of me.* So, I did my best to stand there silently, especially with the man who was standing by her side. I can't be sure, but I believe it was her manager and husband at the time, Jim Martin. Boy, did her husband turn out to be a frightening individual. There were several articles and videos about how he tried to kill her. I read in the *Sports Illustrated* magazine that among other sick and disturbing things he did to her, he also stabbed her several times and then shot Christy with her own pink gun. I'll let you discover the rest of the gory details on your own. Thank goodness for her, she was a tough fighter or she may not have survived his ruthless attacks.

After my initial glance at the fighter and her man, I just looked down and tried to mind my own business. To no one's surprise, Christy was the female who won the fight that night. My boy Roy didn't do too shabby either. It was the first time I had ever seen him fight in person, and I was actually enjoying the boxing match. I had trouble remaining in my seat because I kept wanting to jump up and yell with the crowd. The match was so exciting, and you could feel the wild energy coming from everyone in the building. Of course, plenty of it had to do with Roy's showmanship. He was such a ham! He liked to entertain his fans and get them laughing with silly little movements or gestures he made toward his opponents in the ring. Roy could be very cocky, but he had the record to back it up.

Cheryl and I were fortunate to have been given V.I.P. tickets with amazing ringside seats. Since the seats afforded us the opportunity to see things fairly close up, I found myself having to cover my eyes at times and peek through my fingers so I didn't have to see all the flying sweat and blood. While I started to enjoy the sport of boxing, I still preferred not to look at the gross stuff. The match was incredible, though, and not surprisingly, Roy Jones Jr. reigned victorious again. Roy had already earned the title of "pound for pound the best boxer in the world." His stats were remarkable and there were not many competitors, if any, in his weight class who could touch him. He was an unbeatable, unstoppable, bona fide boxing machine.

The evening was filled with fun and excitement. Cheryl and I even stuck around afterwards and took our picture with Don King, a world-renowned boxing promotor, and his very large hair. He's a bit intimidating as a person, but he was smiling big and cracking jokes the whole time. He was definitely in his element.

The show was over, and since we were staying in Vegas, Cheryl and I decided to venture off and try our hand at our favorite game, craps. I was doing so well rolling the dice, the people around the table were chanting my name. The table was hot, and I was having a great time being the shooter. At least that night we came out ahead with extra money in our pockets and didn't end up losing it all like usual.

We hung around in Las Vegas with our pal Greg and some other friends before finally departing and making our journey home. We had an amazing weekend. I was thankful to get the opportunity to have a one-of-a-kind, fascinating experience. It was yet another extremely memorable moment, and the last time I would see Roy until a few years later.

I was "married *without* children" the next time I went to one of Roy's boxing matches, and my husband Scott was able to come along with me. Roy was going to be fighting in Portland, Oregon this time around. Never having been to Portland before, I was excited for this trip. Scott and I made reservations at The Benson, which was a historic hotel in downtown Portland. It was where Roy and others involved with the fight were staying. The Benson Hotel was an absolute masterpiece of elegance with its spectacular architecture, crystal chandeliers, Italian marble floors, and exquisite staircase. I felt fortunate to get to go on this amazing vacation and stay in such a charming, historical building. I was so overwhelmed that when I saw Roy enter the lobby just as Scott and I were checking in, I had to immediately turn around and thank him for this incredible opportunity. I was also eager to introduce him to my husband Scott since they had never met before.

When I was telling Roy I was really looking forward to seeing him fight, and wishing him good luck (which he really didn't need), he mentioned there would be some sort of surprise at his event I should be looking out for. Of course, I had no idea what he was referring to, but I was definitely intrigued. Even my buddy Greg would not spill the beans about the surprise when I tried to get it out of him. Guess I would have to patiently wait like the rest of the fans.

Scott and I soon made our way up to our quaint little room and unpacked. Then we spent the rest of the evening exploring downtown Portland. It was such a neat city with a plethora of unique restaurants, shops, and bars. For dinner, we found the sweetest little Italian restaurant where we dined on delicious pasta, bread dipped in oil and balsamic vinegar (my favorite), and caprese coupled with a few glasses of red wine. We also splurged on tiramisu, crème brulee, and a warm cup of espresso. With our bellies more than stuffed, and our bodies tired from our day of travel, we decided it was a good time to turn in, back at the hotel.

The next morning, we woke up and had plenty of time to venture around before the big fight, so Scott and I decided to take our rented silver PT Cruiser for a little spin along the Oregon Coast. The ocean looked beautiful. It was quite a bit different than Southern California beaches. There were a lot more hills with beautiful trees and greenery, as well as neat rock formations which stood tall in the ocean waves.

We hiked an incredibly gorgeous path to Short Sand Beach and also explored the stunning surroundings and beautiful cascading waterfall at Secret Beach. While all the beaches and landscapes were remarkable, my favorite one to visit was Haystack Rock in Cannon Beach. It was really cool to see the famous rock from the movie, *Goonies*. Several years later, Scott's dad and step-mom became part owners of a beach house near Haystack Rock. So, we got to explore it a few more times close up. It was always so beautiful there. The weather and water were a heck of a lot chillier than in Southern California. That aside, the scenery was absolutely gorgeous.

It was a tad cold and cloudy with off and on showers the day we went exploring, but the time spent on our drive was nothing short of fabulous. It was fun touring a new place and turning it into a memorable adventure. After hours of traveling around, we began to feel quite hungry, so we hit a popular pizza and brew pub for a late lunch. Then we decided it was time to get back to our hotel and freshen up before the main event of the evening.

It was Saturday night and we were all dressed and ready to head out for the big fight. There was already a huge crowd when we walked into the Rose Garden (which was renamed the Moda Center shortly after) and found our seats. The place was packed, and the energy was high. As the boxing match was about to begin, we watched Roy's competitor, Clinton Woods, walk through the dark hallway, make his way through the crowd, and up onto the stage into the boxing ring. Next, we stood at the ropes watching and waiting for Roy to come out of the other tunnel. It was taking a while, and the crowd started wondering what was wrong. Then all of a sudden, music started blaring, and a spotlight was aimed at the very top of the stadium. Out of the dark and into the bright spotlight came Roy Jones Jr. in all his glory, rapping for the crowd as he made his way down the stadium. Everyone went nuts! It was fun watching Roy rap while making his way down the steps and eventually into the ring. He put on a good show and certainly delighted his fans, especially me.

Though I knew Roy liked hip-hop music and rapping, I was not expecting things to go down like that before his boxing match. However, it made a lasting impression I'm certain no one at the fight that night could possibly forget.

After the fun and laughter had subsided, it was time to get down to business. The boxing match was about to begin, and Roy had to transform from one character into another. He took off his shiny robe, immediately put on his game face, and got the fight rolling. As usual, he taunted his opponent and made some smart remarks as he shuffled around him in the ring. I came to learn that Roy was quite a silly guy who enjoyed teasing and having fun. This fight was no different. He threw in humor where he could but then solidly landed his punches. As several lively rounds went on, I began to get a little nervous for Roy. I'm sure he knew what he was doing though. The guy did not know how to lose a fight. It finally came to an end, and we were able to witness Roy become the champion once again. It was great to get to celebrate another win and be in such a charming city at the same time.

Scott and I woke up early Sunday morning in order to make the most of our trip to Portland. We walked out of our hotel and hit a cool coffee shop as we toured around the main streets. One of my favorite things to do was to sit on the steps in the middle of Pioneer Courthouse Square, and simply chill while checking out the people and our surroundings. We also visited a couple of used bookstores, which were unique little places. I really enjoyed browsing around in them since there is nothing compared to those bookstores where I live.

Waterfront Park was another neat attraction to see and explore. I wish we could have been there for one of the blues festivals though. I'm sure the music and atmosphere would have been amazing. It sure was beautiful to walk around and look at all of Portland's culture and check out its historical monuments and scenic riverfront.

Later on, we cruised around the blocks near Pioneer Courthouse Square, exploring the variety of shops. Although we should have gone to the Ringside Steakhouse (just for its name alone) for dinner, we decided to stay closer to our hotel and settled for a fun little gastropub instead.

Monday morning, we sadly had to get up and prepare for our flight home. We had such an incredible vacation visiting Portland and getting to see another one of Roy's fights. I was already looking forward to going back and visiting the quaint downtown area again. Along with the amazing restaurants, shops, and more, it was a cool city to see and tour. I hope someday soon we'll get another opportunity to visit that fabulous place.

Round 3

ROLL WITH THE PUNCHES

Quite some time had passed since I had gone to any of Roy's boxing matches in person, so I would do my best to catch them on TV when I could. However, life had crept up on me and somehow things become busier than ever. By this time, my massage career had unfortunately come to an end, and I was working feverishly to get my new career off and running. I had to roll with the punches since there was no choice other than to leave massage due to an unfortunate car accident.

While driving home after visiting some friends in Newport Beach, a semi-truck plowed over me on the 91 Freeway. Traffic was always bad on the 91 and this day wasn't much better. I had been cruising along at the normal speed limit, which was 55 mph back then, driving in the right-hand lane of the freeway. Remember Sammy Hagar's song "I Can't Drive 55"? Believe it or not, I actually did. I was being responsible and obeying the speed limit. Then all of a sudden, out my driver's side window, I turned and noticed a gigantic white beast coming right toward me. I screamed out loud and then was hit and pushed off onto the right shoulder of the road. The whole thing happened within seconds, yet it felt as if it was all taking place in slow motion. It was exactly the way they show it in the movies. Hard to explain, but it was most definitely how it feels when you are in that moment. Your brain experiences things slowly as everything else moves rapidly around you. Luckily for me, the semi hit my car in just the right place, or I most likely would have been smashed underneath the giant monster of a truck.

Shocked at what had just occurred, I sat there paralyzed and watched through my rear-view mirror a dirty, sweaty, mean-looking man run quickly up to my vehicle. He immediately started yelling at me and tried to act as if the accident was somehow my fault. Not surprisingly, I was proven innocent. I didn't even recall him asking if I was okay. He was so scary and unkind as I sat there hurt, crying, and frightened over what had just happened. I had never been in any kind of car accident before. Soon after, more people pulled over to check on us, and someone eventually got to a call box to locate the police. Believe it or not, cell phones were not readily available at the time. We were informed that it was a really busy day, and it would take a long time before help could arrive.

After waiting for what seemed like forever and a day, I idiotically decided to drive home. I was still in total shock and probably did not make the best decision, but thank goodness I arrived home in one piece, then my parents drove me to the hospital. Luckily, I didn't have any broken bones, however, I suffered from a horrible case of whiplash, some bone bruising, and nerve damage, causing the ultimate end to my much-loved sports massage career.

In hindsight, I am now thankful the accident forced me to embark on a new career and led me to meet and eventually marry my love, who is still my husband today. We are now approaching almost 20 years of marriage, and I can honestly say I love him more each day. Though I didn't feel this way when the accident happened, I am now certainly grateful for the shift that took place that led to our meeting.

After my car accident, I didn't know what I would do next. One day, my parents were having a party at their house and a good friend of theirs, Carol, asked me what I thought I wanted to do since massage wasn't an option. Carol was a principal of an elementary school at the time. She persuaded me to consider teaching since I had a long line of educators in my family. My grandfather Pete DiPaolo was a superintendent in a small town in Illinois called Coal City, although I always teased my dad about it being his cover up for really working for the Italian Mafia. My grandfather died before I ever got a chance to meet him, but the pictures I've seen of the family are very old-school Italian. Some of the members in the family look slightly questionable. After constantly joking about it, my dad finally admitted there was an uncle and cousin they highly suspected (or knew) was in the mafia. So, I continue to playfully tease him about his dad. How could I not?

My Grandpa Pete's wife, Kay DiPaolo, was a middle school English teacher in Coal City too. Writing was definitely a passion of hers. I guess that was where I picked up my own love of writing. We wrote letters back and forth to each other until the day she passed away at 95 years old. My grandparent's daughter Jeanine, my dad's youngest sister, is an educator as well. She moved out to California from Illinois like my dad and has been a professor at a university for over 30 years.

My father Dave DiPaolo originally moved out to California from Coal City to teach. He was initially hired at Corona High School as a business teacher, then he moved toward becoming an activities and athletic director. He had such a fun time doing those jobs. I can remember being three years old and going with him and his leadership group to help paint the Prado Dam near Corona, California. To this day, it is a well-known mural easily seen off the 91 and 71 Freeway interchange heading east toward Riverside. If you have ever driven that direction on the freeway before, you have definitely seen the painted dam. It was said to be six times the size of Mt. Rushmore and was the largest Patriotic Mural in the United States. Unless you were blind or asleep, there was no way you could have missed the gigantic painting. There was, and currently as I am writing this in 2020 is, a battle still going on to preserve the Prado Dam's Bicentennial Mural. My dad's group has been working together to get the mural recognized as a landmark with historical significance, which I for one believe it deserves.

When they celebrated the finished mural in May of 1976, Indian tribes, a few individuals, and other groups spoke about the importance of the Bicentennial and taught us more about American history. I can vividly remember taking my picture with a famous actor who played an Indian named Iron Eyes Cody. He was well-known in Bob Hope's film *The Paleface* as Chief Iron Eyes. What I remember Iron Eyes Cody best for was the commercial where he shed a tear over people littering. That really pulled on my heart strings. He was my first introduction to the Native American culture. Having experiences like that were wonderful because I learned early on to love and appreciate other ethnicities different from my own.

To me, the mural on the dam is more than just a beautiful work of art. It has an important message that represents our country's freedom. Based on how much it means to many individuals, my dad has been working with a group to help preserve the original mural. Two of my dad's leadership students, Ron Kammeyer and

Perry Schaefer, worked together to design the famous mural. Then his entire leadership group along with several other volunteers helped paint the dam, which is most definitely faded but still happily visible today.

After doing an impressive job as an activities and athletic director, my dad was coaxed into becoming an assistant principal. Finally, he moved up to human resources at the district office and retired after 38 years with the Corona-Norco School District. My mother, on the other hand, started out as a fourth-grade teacher. Then she quit teaching to stay home and raise us four children. My poor mother. I don't know what she was thinking wanting to stay home with crazy twin boys and two other kids to take care of (more like run interference with).

When my younger sister went into kindergarten, my mom went back to work as a kindergarten teacher. That job was probably a breeze compared to what she put up with dealing with my siblings and me on a daily basis. When I was older, I would often help my mom in her classroom. She was an incredible kindergarten teacher. I believe she learned her remarkable amount of patience with those kids from having to raise us. We were certainly a handful.

Although it was not initially the field I wanted to go into, I guess education was just in my blood. There was no escape. My sister Kara became a school counselor right after college, and my brother Mark recently changed careers to become a counselor as well. He originally followed in the footsteps of our Grandfather Doc, and chose to go to law school right away. After being a criminal defense lawyer for several years, he realized his heart was more with the children as he was a wonderful father to two terrific boys. He also had done some substitute teaching after high school and seemed very gifted in that field. His wife Missy, on the other hand, has continued to stay in law because she is a badass prosecutor. I certainly would not want to go up against her. Missy is awesome at what she does, and I am glad we have someone like her to put away the bad guys. My brother Doug was the only one in our family who did not end up with a job involving education. Instead, he began his career as a chiropractor and later decided it wasn't the right fit for him. Therefore, he switched careers and became an engineer. Everyone in my family is successful and happy with what they are doing now.

After completing my massage certifications, I was asked to be an instructor at my school leading the 100-hour Swedish American course. I co-taught other classes as well. Teaching massage was a passion of mine. I really enjoyed that part of the business, so it made sense to go back to school and earn a teaching credential. Becoming a teacher was ultimately how I ended up meeting my amazing husband Scott—I cannot complain about the necessary change in careers one bit.

Since my dad was currently working for the district office, he and our friend Carol, who was the principal I mentioned earlier, took a trip to Illinois in hopes of recruiting some good teachers for our district. They liked and hired Scott on the spot with a few other teachers as well. My dad would always beam when telling me about the Illinois kids he would hire. He loved anyone from Illinois State because it was his alma matter. I pretended to be interested when he described the recruits from Illinois who would be coming out to teach in California, though I didn't exactly share the same excitement. Had I known then one of them was to become my husband, I may have paid closer attention. It didn't seem to matter though. Destiny, fate, or whatever it was, definitely had its hooks in us.

My dad first introduced Scott and me at the new teacher in-service. I remember immediately feeling drawn to his energy but tried to act as if I didn't care. I had to be cool, right? Next, I found out that Scott and I were going to be working at the same school. I was hired to teach second grade, and he was going to be teaching sixth grade. We helped each other set up our classrooms and spent most every day touring around town together. When people inquired about my relationship with Scott, I demanded that we were just friends, until one day when my sister asked, "If you are just friends, why don't you hook me up?" She said I shot her the look of death after her question. Case closed. After only a few weeks of hanging out, we became inseparable, and the rest is history.

After about a year and a half of dating, Scott and I (meaning, I) decided to get married on a boat in the Newport Beach Harbor. Not being married in a church went against my Catholic upbringing. My dad would joke and sometimes tell people I was the rebel of the family, which was hilarious because I was a total goody-goody. I only broke the rules a couple of times. All my friends know I am typically a major rule follower, but not where my wedding was concerned. I was determined to make it special the way I envisioned it. Normally, I was pretty compliant, but I definitely stood strong for things I believed in. To me, my wedding day was something that was definitely worth fighting for.

I ended up winning the battle, and Scott and I were soon married on the beautiful yacht *Athena* in Newport Beach. One thing I did regret was not being able to have my great uncle, who was a Catholic priest, officiate the wedding. I understood it was something he couldn't do since I chose to have my wedding outside of the church. It was sad, but I had to honor my uncle for staying true to his dedication and devotion to God and the church. Likewise, I hoped people would respect my decision to be married where I felt most comfortable. The ocean has forever been my happy place. It made sense to me to embark on my new life with Scott in the place that always brought me positive vibes and made me light up with pure, joyful energy.

As Scott and I wished, instead of being married by a priest in the Catholic Church, we were married on a boat in the ocean by Captain Benjamin. It sounds silly, but our wedding could not have been more fitting for the two of us. There was nothing else I would have changed about one of the most special days of my life. We had gorgeous flowers, mouthwatering Mexican food, a beautifully decorated and delicious cake, a life-sized R2-D2 ice sculpture, great music, and amazing family and friends. It was not exactly traditional (we walked down the aisle after being pronounced husband and wife, to the theme song from Star Wars), but our wedding was definitely made for us.

After about four years of marriage, being free, running around, spending money, and doing whatever the hell we wanted, we decided perhaps we should consider slowing things down. You can only sit around drinking, eating popcorn, watching movies, and playing video games for so long. Really, I think we were just practicing the games so we could get good enough to play with our kids when we had them. At least, that's the excuse you should be giving if you are still an adult playing video games like Scott and I sometimes did (do). It's really just for the kids, I swear.

Speaking of kids, we eventually had an incredible son named Maverick and a beautiful little girl named Macie Jayne. I love my children more than you could ever imagine, but unfortunately it was the problems which occurred both during and after my pregnancies that led to my debilitating postpartum depression. The depression, while horrible, was instrumental in helping me discover my life altering change through boxing. But first let me explain some of the factors that led up to the initial cause of postpartum depression.

When I was 32 years old, I became pregnant with my son, Maverick. Yes, I am aware that was a little late for having my first child. In spite of my age, I had no real issues with the pregnancy other than your typical morning sickness (which lasted all day and night). They really ought to think about changing the name to "all day and night sickness," as most women know it rarely occurs only in the morning. Anyhow, my pregnancy was all right. Near the end, I turned into a bundle of nerves feeling contractions which may or may not have been

Braxton Hicks. It was always so hard to tell. One particular night on January 24, I started having serious contractions, and they weren't going away. Still 11 days out from my actual due date, I tried to be tough and make it through the night. The next morning around 6:00, I couldn't take it anymore. In a pathetic whining whimper, I let Scott know it was time to drive me to the hospital.

Off we went headed over to Riverside. When we walked into the nursing area, I was asked a series of questions before they would consider taking me back into a room. One of the nurses squinted at me and said quite frankly, "If you are still smiling and talking, you probably aren't ready to deliver your baby." Her statement wiped the grin off my face pretty fast. At this point, I knew I was having "real" contractions and wanted to be monitored in a safe environment.

Eventually, they admitted me and began to run a number of tests. After checking to see if I was dilated or not, the doctor informed me I was only at a number two, and it wasn't quite enough to keep me in the hospital. I argued a bit (in a respectful way) because I was sincerely afraid of leaving. I wanted to be in a safe place where professionals knew how to take care of me since I was in a lot of pain. Instead, I was told my baby wasn't ready to meet the world yet, and I was instructed to go home.

It was a serious struggle walking from the hospital out to our Honda Pilot SUV, (which was an upgrade since a two-seater was no use to a new family of three), but I did as I was told. On the way home, I called my mom and explained to her what had happened. Then I asked if she could meet me at my house for some extra support. The drive home was extremely painful as my contractions were hitting me one after another. No matter how I shifted and turned, I could not get comfortable in my seat. My poor husband had to sit there and listen to me cry and moan all the way home without being able to do anything about it.

Soon enough, we arrived back at our house, and Scott walked over to my side of the car and helped ease me out of my seat. Then he carefully put his arm around me, helped me walk into the house, and gently guided me over to the sofa. It wasn't long before tears started flowing, and I was screaming again with pain. My mom became extremely concerned and demanded we call the hospital back right away. My husband got on the line with one of the nurses, and even though I didn't want to talk, she insisted he put me on the phone. The nurse advised me to take a warm shower and try to eat a little something. So, while my husband was helping me in the shower because I obviously could not do it alone, my mom was downstairs whipping me up a plate of scrambled eggs and toast. She figured eggs would be something simple enough to eat and wouldn't upset my stomach (any more than a baby getting ready to come out would).

Taking a shower was never as hard as it was at that moment. I can still remember it like it was yesterday. I barely made it through with all the immense pain I was feeling. There were streaks of pain and what felt like lightning bolts shooting throughout my entire body. We were lucky I didn't collapse and fall down in the shower. I feared it was exactly what was going to happen. Thankfully, I made it out safely. It was a slow and tedious process, but with the help of my sweet husband, I was able to step out of the shower and get myself dressed.

I made my way downstairs and, following the nurse's orders, I tried having a little bite to eat. My food was hardly finished before the most intense contractions hit me again. Both Scott and my mom had to help me over to the couch. The pain was torturous, though I remember the worried look on my mom's face as I was gripping onto the couch, screaming and crying, and holding on for dear life. She demanded once more that we call the hospital back. This time, my husband had a much more serious, concerned demeanor and tone when speaking to the nurse on the other line. When she asked Scott to put me on the phone again, I refused to talk to her because I couldn't breathe or stop myself from crying.

Less than an hour later from when we initially arrived, we were right back in our Pilot heading to the hospital again. When we exited the car, I could hardly make the walk at all. Due to the contractions, we had to stop every few feet. I gripped onto Scott as tightly as I could until the pain of the contractions passed. Poor guy must have endured serious bruises the way I was squeezing and holding onto him each moment a contraction hit.

After making our way slowly through the dreaded parking lot, we had finally made it into the building. We had almost reached the elevator when another mind-altering contraction came. I frantically watched the elevator doors open and shut as I stood there paralyzed, unable to move. The elevator was only about two feet away from us. All I would've had to do was make a small leap to get inside. There was no way it was happening. The pain was too strong, and I could not move a single muscle. Instead, I stood there hugging Scott tightly and prayed for the paralyzing pain to stop. Watching those elevator doors open and close again right in front of me felt like arriving late to a train station, standing on the platform, watching it depart slowly, while leaving you helplessly behind. I desperately needed to get on the elevator. I had a strong grip on Scott, and he quietly held onto me holding me up while we frantically waited for the elevator to make it back down to our floor again. When the doors finally opened once more, Scott was able to help move me forward. He escorted me inside the elevator so we could begin to make the necessary trek to the nurse's station.

The elevator doors widened, and we stepped out slowly. Then we carefully made our way through the hallway and up to the counter. They asked me a series of questions again, but this time they admitted me immediately, thankfully. The nurses could clearly see my facial expression had changed immensely from before. I was no longer capable of talking or smiling at this point. All I could do was shake my head yes or no, breathe, and cry.

One of the nurses quickly walked me into a room. I barely had enough time to put on my gown before I started visibly struggling with unbearable pain. The nice breakfast my mother had so graciously made for me was coming up faster than it had gone down. As I opened the bathroom door, a couple of nurses rushed in to help me over to the bed. They quickly hooked me up to a monitor and immediately noticed my baby's heart rate was dropping rapidly. Before we really knew what was going on, my water broke, and I was being rushed down a long hallway on a gurney, hearing the nurses say we needed to prep for emergency surgery. I couldn't see Scott anywhere. All I saw were the bright, florescent lights glaring at me from the ceiling above as they whisked me away from my best friend and partner. I was never given the chance to talk to him or say good-bye. Completely scared out of my wits, I wanted my husband there with me. Unfortunately, it was not an option due to the mad rush they were in during this critical moment. A nurse nicely assured me someone would update my husband as soon as they could, and when everything was safe, they would allow him to join me.

When I arrived in the operating room, the nurse quickly rolled me onto my side, instructed me to act like a cat, and hunch my back up so the spinal anesthesia could be administered. Let me tell you how NOT great I was at being a good kitty. I tried to do what she asked, but I was panicked and not exactly trying to win an Oscar for my acting skills. However, I believe the scream I delivered when the needle first went in could have won me such an award.

My whole body felt the tinge of electric shocks surging through it. *Oops!* The anesthesiologist missed. Oh my god, they were going to have to try putting the needle in again. I was beyond frightened at this point. My entire body was convulsing as the nurse held my hands and repeatedly addressed the importance of arching my back. If I could have gotten out if it, I would have. But time was of the essence, so I did my due diligence to be the best cat ever and hunch my back up as far as I could. Guess what? It happened again. The electric shocks streamed throughout my body. My mind went straight to picturing the cats you see in cartoons getting electrocuted. Their fur spikes up and stands on end, the x-ray of their skeleton flickers in black and white, their eyes pop out of their head, and they let out a loud, painful *ME-OOOOOW*. That was exactly how I felt, convulsing and shaking with complete, unadulterated, and sustained fear. I imagined I had been struck by lightning. We had no other option than to attempt the spinal again, so I prayed extensively for the third time to be a charm. Instead of having me lie on my side, the nurse sat me up and held on tight to my shaking knees and legs. Screw the cat—my back was going to be hunched like a wild, ferocious tiger on steroids! Thank goodness in the name of Jesus with a big, fat *hell yeah* and a *hallelujah,* the third time worked like a charm.

Once the spinal took effect, I was placed under a big, blue tarp-like sheet. My husband was finally brought into the operating room and was swiftly escorted under the sheet right up near my head. The nurses were protecting him from having to see any incisions being made or any of the other gore that comes with having a C-section, let alone one that is an emergency.

After a few minutes of working quickly and diligently, they safely pulled our son out of my tummy and allowed my husband to cut the umbilical cord. Afterwards, while the nurses were cleaning our baby boy up, Scott crawled back under the blue sheet-like tent with me, rubbed my head, and smiled as I laid there motionless hardly able to even whisper. It was an extremely traumatic experience I was happy to put behind me. When the nurses brought Maverick over to me all wrapped sweetly and swaddled tight, they leaned him down toward my face, and asked if I wanted to give him a kiss. I was so exhausted and expunged from the trauma and stress I had just been put through, I didn't even have it in me to kiss my own baby. My lips may have touched his precious head, but it certainly wasn't from any of my doing. That was something I will always remember and regret. More than anything, I was just grateful we were both safe and alive.

Round 4

SUCKER-PUNCHED

Maverick was a precious baby boy who I was extremely grateful to have in my life. If I am being completely honest though, it took me a little while to truly bond. When I first brought him home from the hospital, I was feeling helpless. Never having a baby before, I didn't quite know what to do with this teeny, tiny "thing" who was now completely and totally my responsibility. Without the amazing support of my husband and mother, I honestly don't know what I would have done.

This was all brand new to me, and I needed a lot of help and guidance to get me through it. I know that I spent some time babysitting when I was younger, but I didn't recall having to watch many infants. Beyond learning how to breastfeed so my nipples wouldn't bleed, scab, or fall off, I also had to learn the proper way to swaddle my baby. In addition, I needed to learn the right technique to change his diaper because one wrong move could be disastrous. Besides all the runny, green poop that gets all over their backs, boys come equipped with fire hoses that can spray pee all over you if you are not prepared for it. It only took me about once or twice of getting sprayed in the face with the warm splatter before some smart person taught me how to put a clean diaper underneath the dirty one. Then you would have it ready to cover the fateful fountain as soon as the dirty diaper was removed. Genius! How did I not know that? It was those little tips and secrets I learned along the way that made a big difference in my level of sanity.

Other helpful tricks I learned were to put my baby in the stroller and walk him around the house to try to get him to stop crying and fall asleep. I also would put Maverick in the car and drive him around the block sometimes to get him to take a nap. You'll pretty much do anything to make a baby stop crying. Those were just a couple strategies I used that helped me not lose my mind.

After I got the tips and tricks down, things were much better, and I finally felt like I was bonding with my baby boy. Once I had some things under control, I was able to start enjoying him the way I had expected to when he was first born. It took some time before I actually believed I was doing a decent job and being a good mother. Being a new mom was hard—definitely not something to scoff about. Though times could be challenging, I learned to love my new role as a mother. Maverick became my everything.

After about four months with my precious baby boy, it was time for me to go back to work where I was teaching kindergarten at a public elementary school. The thought of leaving my baby with someone else while I was gone all day was gut-wrenching. Thank goodness, I found the best babysitter ever. Next door to one of my good friends Adrianna, who you will hear more about later, lived an incredible lady who had just been considering watching children part time.

My husband and I scheduled a day to meet with Adrianna's neighbor Dee. We were a bit nervous at first. It was a huge ordeal to be considering leaving our baby with a mere stranger all day. However, we felt so much better and simply put at ease after just a few moments of meeting with Dee. After the interview was complete, Scott and I walked out of her house smiling, feeling like there was no need to look any further. Mama Dee was the perfect fit, and I could not have asked for a better daycare provider. She loved to spoil my son, and when I called her on it, she just laughed at me. I loved and appreciated her for it. Having someone to truly love and take care of my boy made it slightly less painful to head back into the workforce.

Once I was back at work, I got to see all my little cutie-pie students, was in a normal routine, and I felt blessed. I enjoyed being a teacher, a wife, and now a mother. The roughest parts were behind me, and I believed I was doing a decent job at handling this motherhood thing. Maverick was a good baby, and I was enjoying this part of my life. Although having kids was certainly life altering, it was becoming my new normal, and I could not complain one bit.

A couple of years went by, then Scott and I decided we didn't want to have an only child. We really wanted Maverick to have siblings like we did growing up. Both of us came from decent-sized families. I had twin brothers who were two years older than me and a sister who was born four years after me. Yes, I am a middle child, and I wouldn't have it any other way. My husband, also a middle child, had one older sister, one younger sister, a younger half-brother and sister, and a step-brother and sister.

While things weren't always peaches and cream, we both enjoyed all the experiences we had with our siblings and wanted the same kind of life for our son. Therefore, it was extremely heart-wrenching and debilitating the day my OBGYN informed me it could be life-threatening for me to carry another baby. It felt as if I had just been sucker-punched. I certainly was not prepared for that kind of hit.

Originally, I made an appointment to see my gynecologist because I was having a difficult time getting pregnant again. I had suffered from a couple of early miscarriages, one in which a dilation and curettage (D&C) was necessary at eight weeks. We had been working on another baby for more than a year and a half. It was taking a very long time trying to conceive and hang on to the pregnancy, without any luck, so I met with my OBGYN.

My doctor carefully examined my history, which included very painful menstrual cycles, surgery for cervical cancer, miscarriages, and an emergency C-section. There was a lot going on in my womanly arena. I did mean to say "arena" and not "area." My insides felt like an arena with all kinds of moving parts and crazy activities going on in there. Many traumatic experiences had taken place in that region of my body. One of my doctors even had to explain to me that my cervical cancer was caused by sexual activity. I was completely dumfounded because I wasn't having any sexual escapades before being told I had the cancer, though, I had been sexually assaulted at the young age of 14. That's a whole story in itself, one which was so traumatizing that I didn't tell anyone about it for four years. So, that unfortunately was how I ended up with cervical cancer. With everything I had been through, my doctor decided performing a laparoscopy would be the next feasible step. It would help her get a better look inside to see what was going on and find out what was preventing me from having another baby.

After the results of the laparoscopy came back, the doctor sat both Scott and me down to show us pictures and explain what had actually been taking place inside my "arena of wonder." First, she pointed out the areas where I had endometriosis. Typically, a diagnosis of endometriosis is bad enough, and very painful. But that wasn't the only thing wrong. Damn, couldn't I have been let off easy for once? Next, the doctor lowered her tone and began to speak to us in a tender but sorrowful voice. She showed us both the "severe" case of scar tissue, which developed from my emergency C-section with Maverick. The scar tissue looked like thick, wide spider webs connecting my uterus to my abdominal wall. Due to the severity of the scar tissue, my doctor said it could be life-threatening to have another baby.

This news was shattering to both of us. We were in shock and disbelief. The thought of not being able to have a sibling for Maverick seemed unfathomable and devastating. Those were not the words we went in preparing to hear. We walked into her office hopeful, thinking we would have answers and a solution. Instead, we walked away feeling helpless and destroyed.

The car ride home from the hospital was somber to say the least. We both fought back tears as we discussed the reality of not being able to have another baby. While we were grateful and blessed to have Maverick in our lives, we still had hoped to add another child to our family to love as much as we already loved and adored him. The thought of it being the end weighed heavily on our hearts, but we understood there was nothing we could do under the circumstances.

Less than two months after I had the laparoscopy (which helped the doctor peek inside and also removed most of the endometriosis), we encountered another problem. We did not recall being told the removal of endometriosis usually made women quite fertile. We clearly must have been off on our timing because a major "oops" happened. I mean a really big, fat, frightening "oh my god, what are we going to do now" kind of oops. I'm sure you can guess what I'm referring to. This was far beyond anything I ever expected. I was officially late and nervously awaiting that special aunt to arrive, you know, the one who we normally dread a visit from. Except there tend to be those occasional times in life when we are elated to see her. This was one of them, but she let me down. She must have listened to all those times when I wanted to go have fun at the beach and begged her not to come.

After realizing my aunt may truly not be stopping by for a visit this month, I figured I had better pick up a test, the one with the plus or minus sign, one or two lines, and the words "yes or no." I peed on a stick, and then another stick, and even another stick to be completely sure. Each time, two pink lines showed up. Yes indeed, there was no denying it—undoubtedly, I was pregnant. Oh my god, I was actually pregnant! While my whole entire being wanted to explode with excitement, my mind said, *Oh no, this is really bad! What am I going to do?* This was a so-called life-threatening situation and decision. My emotions were beyond normal comprehension. I didn't know how I was supposed to feel other than being overjoyed and extremely petrified at the same time. Those emotions, while both very real ones, did not go well together.

After talking through everything with my husband, I decided to call my mom for some good old-fashioned advice. Mothers are the best at that, and also at being an incredible comfort when you need it, at least that's the way I felt about my mom. We discussed the situation for a while and my mom came up with a brilliant idea. She advised me to seek guidance from my sister's OBGYN, since he was a specialist in the field.

When my sister Kara was delivering her first son Adam, she had some serious complications. She stayed in the hospital and went through hard labor for about three days. She eventually had to be induced, which was not proving to be very effective. So, they had to use a suction device in order to get her baby out. During the early hours of 3:00 a.m., Kara started hemorrhaging. A specialist was brought in to handle the dangerous situation, and she ended up having to get a blood transfusion. It was a scary ordeal.

I vividly remember going to visit her in the hospital. Her skin was as pale, white as a ghost, and her lips were bluish purple. She looked and sounded like she was barely alive. It was a tough scene to take in. Thankfully, her baby boy Adam was okay, and Kara eventually made a full recovery.

Due to Kara's medical trauma, I was able to meet with her specialist and get his opinion about my troublesome situation. Kara had an appointment scheduled with her OBGYN, Dr. Berberich. She had asked him if it was alright for me to come along with her to the appointment to get his advice. Dr. Berberich was one of the kindest doctors ever and told my sister he would be happy to offer his help.

I could feel the butterflies and nerves in my stomach as Kara and I drove to her appointment together. Whatever the doctor said was ultimately going to be my fate. Knowing the dangers of carrying a baby were weighing heavily on me, there was a raging debate going on in my head about whether or not I should risk my own life to have this child, and mine wasn't the only life I would be putting in danger. Both the baby and I could be at risk if I chose to continue with the pregnancy.

Kara and I waited our turn. As I sat nervously with a big manilla envelope of pictures on my lap, Kara reached over and put her hand on top of mine to try and calm me down. We looked at each other with a smile of question and uncertainty, but also felt somehow everything would be okay. I had to let it all go as it was out of my control.

We hadn't been in the waiting room very long (which was unusual for Dr. Berberich, as he was famously known for taking a long time), when a nurse opened up the door and called us inside. We then sat waiting in the examining room for Dr. Berberich to arrive. By this time my nerves were shot. It was immensely tough to hold it together.

After Dr. Berberich checked in with my sister, he pulled up a chair in front of me. Then in a soft, deep, but serious voice asked, "Now, how can I help you?" I pulled the pictures from my laparoscopy out of the manilla envelope and explained my situation. He silently studied the pictures for a bit. Then I timidly asked, "Do you think there is any way I would be able to keep my baby?" After asking my question, Dr. Berberich paused a moment, then looked up at me slowly and said, "I think I can get you through this." What? Did I hear him correctly? Did this nice man just say he could get me through this? He never showed he was annoyed when I questioned him over and over again. "Are you absolutely sure it is okay for me to have this baby because I was told..." Dr. Berberich continued to reassure me he could get me through my pregnancy and was willing to take me on as a patient.

This was the best answer and outcome I could have possibly hoped for. After thanking Dr. Berberich immensely for his help and kindness in agreeing to meet with me, I turned and walked out of the room with a ginormous grin from ear to ear. As Kara and I began to drive home, all I could focus on was the extreme excitement I would get to feel after telling my husband and mother the good news. This was the best day EVER!

Round 5

Going Head to Head

While I wish I could say that my pregnancy was easy and everything was certain to be okay, it unfortunately would be a lie. Though I have often felt envious of the women who say they loved being pregnant, how it was the most wonderful experience in the world, and that they would do it over again in a heartbeat, I still found it slightly bizarre. Not to take anything away from those women, but I simply could not relate. The most enjoyable part of being pregnant for me (other than constantly feeling free to fulfill my cravings of chocolate milkshakes and french fries) was being able to feel the baby kick, though, sometimes it could be just as uncomfortable as it was cool.

In case you weren't aware, some babies become professional athletes while in the womb. They tend to have a special ability to kick or punch you with a lot of power in just the right place. When that happens, it can hurt like a bitch. They find specific areas and tunnels inside your body you didn't even know about. You would think those areas would be out of their reach. They even have the know-how to find those places where their hand or foot really doesn't belong. Beyond feeling something high up in my ribcage, I would occasionally have to run to the restroom and make sure there wasn't a little body part dangling out. Pardon me for the gruesome visual, but it was exactly how it felt sometimes.

Despite all the sickness and discomforts most of us go through during those nine-plus months, at least we come out with the most magnificent prize in the end. It makes it all worth it, we forget about the pain, and we sometimes are even crazy enough to repeat it all over again. Will we ever learn?

Speaking of the end, my nine long months could not have been over fast enough as the due date drew near. This pregnancy, while overwhelming from the start, had become rather difficult for me and I had to be monitored closely. Whenever I went to my scheduled checkups with Dr. Berberich, he always remained calm and tried to convince me there was nothing to worry about. I think maybe he should have been the one to win the Oscar for that performance. I'm certain it took a lot of care and patience to deal with my overactive anxiousness and fear. Thank goodness I had him in my corner. I felt secure in knowing that he truly cared about me and had my best interest at heart.

There were only two weeks left until my actual due date, but we had scheduled a C-section a week before that. Due to the severity of my case, Dr. B. warned me it would be quite dangerous to go into labor and have the baby vaginally, so a scheduled cesarean was imperative.

The Friday before my scheduled surgery, I had one last checkup with Dr. Berberich to make sure everything was going okay as planned. My mother, bless her heart, was kind enough to drive me to my appointment and help me waddle my way into the hospital building. I was definitely walking like a swollen, overweight penguin with a bad back and some stiff legs. I felt more like a fat walrus though. It wasn't a pretty sight. Once we made our way into the building, we walked over to the elevators and waited for quite a while. As more and more people gathered near the elevator, looks of concern came across many of their faces. The elevator doors were not opening, and it soon became apparent to everyone there was a problem.

As people started giving up and making their way down the hallway to the stairs, my mom could see the look of panic and desperation on my face. I had barely made it into the hospital on flat ground. How on earth was I going to make it up several flights of stairs? It didn't matter. There was no turning back and no other choice. The elevators had seemingly broken down, and there was no magical flying unicorn in sight to whisk me away.

My mother had just let me know she had left her book in the car. She was definitely going to need that at the rate Dr. Berberich moved. Not wanting to be late for my appointment, I began heading down the hallway on my own. When I finally reached the stairs, I grabbed onto the handrail and started making my way up with all the other people who were unable to ride the elevator as well. I was only capable of climbing one flight of stairs before the huffing and puffing kicked in. It became marginally discouraging as I witnessed much older men and women with walkers, canes, and osteoporosis passing me along the way. Feeling exhausted and sweaty already, I had to do my best to hang on and keep moving forward despite the fact that elderly people were leaving me in the dust. It was slow going, but I eventually made it up to the fourth floor. Even though that doesn't sound like much, it felt as if I had been climbing to the top of the Empire State Building. It practically did me in.

Hardly believing I had actually made it to the waiting room, I found a seat and gradually sat down. Less than a few minutes later, in walked my mom all smiley and happy, without showing any signs of being tired or out of breath. When I started whining and complaining about my pure frustration with the strenuous stairs, she informed me the elevators had started working again. She along with many others were able to ride straight up. I had to hold back my anger because I literally felt like I could have died walking up all those steps. I was thrilled for those in-shape, nonpregnant people who so easily rode the elevator. I was totally jealous, and I wanted to punch and kick them in the oddly painful places my baby had been hitting and kicking me.

When I was *finally* in the office with Dr. Berberich, I tried to explain to him how I was feeling immensely uneasy about being able to hold out until Monday for my scheduled cesarean, especially after struggling to walk up all those flights of stairs. In his usual manner, Dr. B. sincerely tried to assure me I had nothing to be concerned about. Yet, I was one hundred percent convinced I would not make it through the weekend and tried exceptionally hard to get him to understand and believe me. I had to go head to head with him. We went round and round about it for a while, but through all my pleading and tears, I could not persuade him to give in. Even though he understood, the hospital had rules about how early cesareans could be performed—I would have to wait.

After a tiresome effort that got me nowhere, I did the only thing I could think of to convince Dr. B. I was determined and meant business. In the most serious voice ever I said, "I am willing to bet you one hundred dollars I do not make it through the weekend to get to my surgery on Monday." Dr. Berberich shook his head back and forth, laughing at my desperate approach. Most likely just to get me to shut up, he said, "Amy, I am not going to bet you a hundred dollars, but I will agree to bet you a quarter if it makes you happy." At least I had his attention now (or so it seemed like it to me). Next, I held out my hand to shake his and firmly stated, "It's a deal!"

I left the hospital feeling somewhat relieved with the understanding and communication which took place between Dr. Berberich and me. Not that I believed I would make it through the weekend, it was more about the fact he actually took the time to listen. I cried and laughed with him. I honestly think he believed I would be okay and thought I was just a bit worked up from the enormous mountain (steps) I had to climb. We had built a really strong bond throughout the past nine months. He got to know me and my quirks fairly well, and he always showed me grace. Yet, I still truly believed I knew my body best and have had many awful (some even horrendous) experiences with my health where the doctors just wouldn't listen or believe what I was telling them. It was true I did not have a medical degree, but I knew me. Dr. Berberich was one of the first doctors I felt was thoroughly invested in my well-being. All of his patients said the same about him. He was so loved and respected by his patients that they would sit in the waiting room for a very, very long time. Dr. B. was laughingly known to be uber-slow, but when it was your turn to see him, you knew you would have his full attention and be in the best care possible. Many patients, including me, believed he was definitely worth the wait.

It was Friday night, February 18, the same evening after I had miserably climbed up all those flights of stairs and made a quarter-sized bet with my caring and skilled doctor. There was a slight smirk on my face coupled with absolute fear knowing instinctively I was going to prove him wrong. With the way I was feeling, there was no chance I would make it to Monday. Almost as soon as I lie down for bed, the contractions started to hit. *Oh no! I cannot go into labor!* I thought. It could be extremely dangerous for the baby and me. I had to have that nice, easy, scheduled C-section, and was not supposed to go into labor beforehand.

My husband calmly persuaded me to try and relax and take slow, deep breaths. I did as he suggested. Thankfully, the contractions were very light and eased up enough that I was able to fall asleep. Though not to my surprise, around 5:00 a.m. Saturday, February 19, my little baby girl decided she wanted out. The contractions kicked up again, and my husband and I timed each one. Knowing it could be trouble if my contractions became close and I actually went into real labor, we decided it was in everyone's best interest to head over to the hospital. This time around we had to drive to Anaheim which was 30 minutes away.

I was doing fairly well on the ride over. It was more of an anxious feeling than anything. Since it was the weekend, I was worried Dr. Berberich would not be able to perform my surgery. Yet, he was the specialist who was supposed to get me through this and keep my baby and me safe. Dr. B. was a seasoned and extremely skilled surgeon who knew my situation. I did not feel safe with any other doctor. Unfortunately, I didn't really have a choice. This little girl was coming, ready or not, and nothing was going to stop her.

Once we arrived at the Anaheim Hospital, Scott and I checked into labor and delivery. We were escorted to a room where I was immediately hooked up to monitors. My contractions were not painful at all compared to the torturous ones I felt with Maverick. In fact, I was halfway expecting to be sent back home. However, to my surprise, one of the nurses came in, smiled, and said, "It looks like you're going to have your baby today." "Are you serious?" I questioned. She explained in a kind voice, "Yes, these are real contractions, and you are ready to have your baby." I was not actually "ready" to have my baby because my special doctor was not working on Saturday. I had prepared for this and trusted he would be the one taking care of me, and I needed him!

When I was introduced to a sweet, pretty female doctor with long, dark, hair and a kind smile, who warmly shook my hand, I still felt slightly apprehensive and scared. She nicely let me know she was the one who would be doing my surgery and asked if I had any questions. At first, I didn't know what to say. The doctor had a wonderful bedside manner, but one problem was still standing in the way—she wasn't Dr. Berberich.

Realizing my fate and understanding what had to be done, I turned to the kindhearted, sympathetic doctor and said, "I don't have any questions, but I do have a favor to ask. If you wouldn't mind, could you please call Dr. Berberich and let him know that he owes me a quarter?" She giggled a little at first and was a bit surprised by my request, until I explained the situation. Then she smiled and agreed to do as I asked. With a big sigh, I took a deep breath and began to feel a little better. The next thing you know, I was being prepped for surgery.

Before the actual C-section could take place, of course I had to go through my worst nightmare again— visiting the anesthesiologist in order to get a spinal. This part did not make me happy. It was not a memorable or joyous experience at all. In lieu of what happened to me before, I tried feverishly to put it out of my mind and head into this strong and prepared. Intent on showing proof of my mental toughness, I was ready to hunch my back like the freakiest cat ever. That was until the very first needle went in, and I screamed like a little freakin' baby.

There they were, all those electric shocks again piercing throughout my body. Holy hell, that pain was fierce and it scared the complete crap out of me. No more mental toughness! No more freaky cats! I wasn't doing it! But my luck was running out. Not only was my special doctor not working, but it just so happened the anesthesiologist I got was a rookie. *Oh hell to the f-cking no!* Under no circumstances was I going to let this guy try to stick a needle in my back again. I begged and I pleaded to get out of it. I asked them to put me to sleep. Unfortunately, they were not in agreement with me.

I was shaking nervously, crying and hollering, as they tried the spinal once more. It was not the most pleasurable experience as the needle hit the wrong spot again. By this time, I could not forget about what I had gone through before. The memories came flooding back traumatically. I was shaking and crying, begging to be put under and out of my misery. There was no possible way I could go through this again. With massive tears streaming down my face, I pleaded for them to knock me out. "Please just knock me out! I don't want to do this again! Please, please, please put me to sleep!" I begged. Sadly, I was turned down and my request was denied as the needle was heading toward my spine a third time. Three must have been the lucky number because this time it went into the right spot. As the drugs went through me and numbed my body, I finally began to settle down.

Believe it or not, my luck was about to change. While I was lying down waiting for the spinal to take full effect, in walked a tall, older man with brown hair and a mustache, wearing green scrubs and the same green-colored hair cap to match. I was a bit loopy from the medication, but I recognized this man immediately. It was my Dr. Berberich! Nothing could have made me happier at the moment. I was so surprised and elated to see him. He said he was all scrubbed up and ready to take me into surgery. I couldn't believe what I was seeing or hearing, but I didn't care. Instead, I just gleamed with happiness and felt a sense of peace come over me. It was clear I was going to be in good hands. As grateful as I was for Dr. B. showing up on his day off, I immediately scolded him and shouted, "You owe me a quarter! Now let's go get my baby out!"

As Dr. Berberich was pushing my bed toward the operating room, I asked, "How on earth are you able to be here right now? You don't work on weekends. You told me yourself just yesterday." Dr. B. replied back, "Well, I was actually on the freeway heading to a meeting when I received an interesting phone call. It was one of my fellow co-workers calling to deliver a message saying I owed a girl named Amy a quarter. After hearing the message, I canceled my meeting, got off at the next exit, turned my car around, and headed straight to the hospital."

Oh, my goodness! Who does that? Certainly not any HMO doctor that I've ever known. This tremendous human being went way over and above for his patients. This had to have been divine intervention at its best because this kind of thing just did not happen. I seriously could not believe my lucky stars.

Even though we had to go head to head at first, it quickly became apparent how lucky I was to have Dr. Berberich in my corner. As he was performing the surgery, he noticed a problem with my uterus. The way he described it was I had windows in my uterus (meaning the lining was so thin you could see the baby through it). If the lining would have torn, it would've been game-over for me. I easily could have hemorrhaged to death. I'm sure I would not be here today telling this story. By the grace of God and some very skilled hands, Dr. B. was able to get my baby girl out safely. Then he carefully repaired the damage and sewed up my uterus.

After all was said and done, my precious little wonder was cleaned up and softly handed to me while I was relaxing in the recovery room. Dr. Berberich came in to check on me, then the coolest thing happened. He smiled and said, "Here's the quarter I owe you." He handed over the quarter, and I gladly took it from him and put it in a safe place.

The quarter meant so much more to me than a silly bet, and I can happily state I still have it in a safe place today. It reminds me how grateful and blessed I was to have had the best doctor ever, a beautiful, healthy little girl, and an outstanding husband and family to go along with it. It proved to me that miracles can happen after all.

Round 6

BOXED INTO A CORNER

When I arrived home with my little girl Macie in my arms, I was happy to be in a comfortable place, though I quickly realized I shouldn't have left the hospital so soon. My pain was not under control, and my husband and I didn't have the know-how to take care of it properly. I suffered severely that day and night. It took some time to get my body regulated again after just having major surgery. Eventually, we got the meds working as they should, and I began to slowly feel better. It was a long and painful recovery. Though in the way I mentioned it before, soon I would forget about the absolute hell I went through, and perhaps even consider doing it again. For my own sake, it's probably a blessing the option to have more children was taken away from me. I am quite content and perfectly happy raising the two children I have. There was no need to be greedy, especially when I knew others weren't as lucky. I have had many friends who struggled with fertility and had trouble having one baby, let alone two. I knew how fortunate I was and decided to just be grateful.

Having a baby girl was so exciting to me. I felt l was bonding with her rather easily. Since I already went through many of my firsts with Maverick, it seemed I had a better handle on baby rearing this time around. I knew how to swaddle, change a diaper, and breastfeed without fail. All was going swimmingly well...until it wasn't.

Having one child to care for was challenging enough in its own right. Adding a second doubled the duties, the amount of noise, and added to the number of sleepless nights. While some days were easy and enjoyable, others could be crazy as well as physically and emotionally draining. My patience at times was most definitely tested. Sometimes I handled it with love and grace, other times I lost my sanity and mind.

The first month I spent with Macie as a baby was probably the best. It was very much like the honeymoon phase. We cooed and cuddled, smiled and giggled. At first, I was in love with my new little bundle of joy. She was so sweet and adorable—that was before she learned to scream and cry incessantly.

Shortly after the honeymoon, reality began to creep in, and I turned into someone I didn't like or respect. In every sense of the meaning, I became a zombie robot. I was going through the motions of doing what it took to be a mother without feeling the close bond or emotional connection I should have been experiencing. I literally got up, fed the baby, burped the baby, bathed her, changed her diaper, got her dressed, and prayed she would nap so I could take a much-needed break. Then I would prepare myself to go through the motions time and time again. I performed my duties as a mother like a zombie without expression and fulfilled my responsibilities as a programmed robot would. My heart and true emotions began to slowly dissipate until they were practically nonexistent. That is when the baby blues unfortunately began to set in. Eventually, the depression took over and became much more severe.

Through my own experience along with others I have seen, I believe postpartum depression can happen at various times after giving birth. It also appears to impact mothers on different levels. It most definitely is not a one-size-fits-all type of description. Therefore, it shouldn't be overlooked if someone starts experiencing symptoms weeks or months after a baby is born. There's no telling exactly when or what kind of effect this type of depression can have on a mother. It's safe to say everyone is different in their own respect, so why should a type of depression be classified in the exact same way? Even each pregnancy and baby are very different from one to the next. It only makes sense our experiences, while similar, would not be exactly alike.

The obstacles I faced during my pregnancies and after each baby was born were like night and day. I felt both extremely excited and unbelievably frightened at different times. My emotions were certainly all over the place. I was not the grounded person I wished I could be. Plus, my lack of experience as a mother was all too obvious at times. Clearly, I longed to be a wonderful mother and hoped to live up to the same standards my own mom set, but I struggled with feeling I wasn't doing a good enough job. Perhaps it was all about just taking the time needed to adjust properly instead of expecting to be the perfect mom from the beginning. Why do we put so much pressure on ourselves?

Getting used to being a mom the second time around was hard. Especially with all the trauma and ups and downs I had to go through to have this baby. Plus, I was now responsible for the well-being of not only one, but two little human beings. There was absolutely a period of adjustment I needed to go through. While being a new mom again was fun and exciting, it certainly did not come without challenges.

Thankfully after having Maverick, I was able to stay home and enjoy my time being with him every day for the first four months. Leaving him and going back to work was sad and hard, but I was able to cope with it well enough. Was it because I had time to make those adjustments I needed to as a new mom? Was it because I had the individual alone time to be with my newborn son? Was it because I didn't have another toddler who I was also responsible for when I had Maverick? I'm not sure exactly what the trigger was. All I know is it was a completely different scenario when I tried to return to work after having Macie.

I had been slowly going downhill a couple months after Macie was born. The tiresome routine of caring for both a newborn and a toddler by myself became tedious work. Rarely did I want to leave the house, because it was a major ordeal trying to get both of them ready to go anywhere. Yet sitting at home in isolation was almost just as hard. No matter which way I looked at it, I just couldn't win.

Scott took a couple weeks off work to be with all of us after Macie was born. It was nice having him around. Perhaps that's why I became so depressed shortly after he went back to work. I was truly on my own with two small humans to raise, trying my best to cater to their every need. I loved them immensely, but they also bled me dry at times, leaving me completely depleted and exhausted.

I was able to stay home with Macie a little longer than with Maverick. It was just the way the timing worked out with my job. Going back to work wasn't too much of a problem with Maverick. I figured it might even be easier than staying home with my two little ones. It was actually a good thing to go back to work, have your own identity, and feel like a real human being again. Unfortunately, things didn't work out as well as they had when I first returned to work after having Maverick.

I was teaching second grade at this time, which I believed was slightly easier than kindergarten. The students were obviously more independent at seven years old than they were at five. While they were still needy, they wouldn't typically pull on my clothes, wipe gooey, sticky things on me with dirty hands, or yell "teacher, teacher" every few seconds instead of calling me by name. Regrettably, second graders would still do some of the gross things like pick their noses, wipe snot across their cheeks with their arm, chew their pencils and erasers, or sneeze and cough without covering their mouths. At least when they are seven, they usually try to hide the grossness instead of outwardly doing it with no shame like my kindergarten students. Even with all of the icky and disturbing things they do, I still can't help adore all of my little babies, no matter what age they are. There's just something about each and every one of their unique characters that truly warms my heart. So, I just have to giggle at their nasty little habits.

Even with all the cuteness (and funny little gruesome things), it never fails—there are always a couple students who are more difficult to teach than others. That just goes without saying. Typically, these students are some of my favorites because they challenge me to find a way to help them get better. There is always an underlying reason they act out in class, and it's usually not a happy one.

For example, one year I had a boy who struggled academically, gave me dirty looks every day, would kick my feet, and wasn't very nice to the other kids in class. I initially thought, *What the heck is up with this kid? What is his problem?* Soon enough, I found out exactly what was up with him and what his problem was. When I looked into his background, I found out his entire family, including him, had been hit in their boat on the lake by someone who was driving drunk. Not only did the family members suffer from significant injuries, but the father was killed in the accident that day. My student's older brother ended up in a coma for six months and lost ten percent of his frontal lobe. In addition to the horrible trauma, the family already struggled as my student's sister had a pretty severe case of autism. She often had meltdowns which resulted in uncontrollable screaming or crying. Occasionally, her breakdowns could even become somewhat violent. The family did the best they could, but I know it became quite wearing on them at times. There was so much hardship this sweet family had to endure. It truly broke my heart and made me more understanding when dealing with this boy's tough attitude and wall he had put up around himself.

It was apparent my student was boxed into a corner. How could he not be, with everything he had gone through in his life so far? Not only did he have to live with major trauma from his past, but he also had a learning disability as well as attention deficit/hyperactivity disorder (ADHD). These disabilities were undiagnosed when he first came to me. No doubt school was difficult for him. Plain life for anyone going through that would be hard enough. He had more to deal with in his short seven years of life than many people will ever experience throughout their entire existence. Though it was a lot of work and he tried my patience at times (as even our own kids do), I truly had love and compassion for this boy. His mother and step-dad, as much as they loved him, struggled teaching him too. The difference was they were on board to help and were very supportive. Therefore, as tough as it was, we were able to make some progress. Unfortunately, teachers find that isn't always the case. Sadly, not all parents are as willing to help at home. Luckily for my guy, his mom and step-dad were amazing.

Something I always try to do with my students is to inquire about each individual's likes and interests. It makes it easier to connect with him or her in a way that is meaningful. I found out my student liked to ride dirt bikes and race BMX. He was pretty darn skilled at it too, which was great because he had something to help build his confidence. After a few short months in my class, he unfortunately got into a riding accident and broke several bones. As if things couldn't get any worse for him, he broke his femur, tailbone, and pelvis. Poor guy was in bad shape.

I spoke to his mother daily and went to visit him in the hospital at Loma Linda. Since he was such a huge dirt bike and motocross fan, I contacted my friend Ashley, who was married to a professional rider. Her husband Josh Grant was a famous and highly ranked athlete in both motocross and supercross for several years. All I did was ask Ashley if Josh would be willing to sign an autograph for one of my students who was a big fan. When I went over to her house to get the autograph, I spoke to Josh about the boy in my class who had the bad accident. The guy didn't just sign an autograph, he pulled out one of his jerseys he wore in a race and autographed it for my boy. He even autographed the rest of the gear that went with it. What a generous thing to do. I knew it would certainly help cheer my student up when I delivered it to him during his stay in the hospital. The look on my student's face was priceless when I handed him the autographed jersey and the rest of the gear. In all his discomfort and pain, he could not have looked happier. It was truly amazing to see his smile and eyes light up for a few, brief minutes.

When my little buddy finally was able to leave the hospital and come back to school, he had to be pushed around in a wheelchair. Believe it or not, the attention he received from it helped change him quite a bit. I saw his confidence and self-esteem start to grow.

He smiled as different kids fought over who was going to push him around at recess or on any errands around campus. The tragic accident became a positive experience for him in many ways, but he could still be a stinker when he wanted to. Even though we had created a great bond, he jokingly continued to give me hell from time to time. Just when the gloves were about to come off, he would be saved by the bell.

My student could be an ornery little dude, but I loved and accepted him the way he was. To this day, I am still in close contact with him and his family. He struggles from depression and anxiety here and there as anyone would who has been through as much devastation and trauma as he had. It's a shame I couldn't get him into boxing instead of dirt bikes. In spite of it all, he has persevered through serious struggles and has most assuredly learned how to become a true fighter.

I have had several challenging students before and have handled it well, usually making a positive difference in their lives. Regrettably, the year after having Macie was much different. I had one boy in particular who I couldn't seem to get through to. He came from a seriously dysfunctional family and was quite a handful. He definitely had ADHD and a real mean streak to go with it. I had to put him in his own island so he wouldn't hurt other kids. Instinctively, I told him it was his special place so the other students wouldn't be able to bother him. That way he didn't feel isolated and actually liked his "special island" area. I even went as far as to create a little blue ocean around his desk.

I seriously practiced every trick in the book I knew to try to help this child and also keep my other students safe. Knowing his family was a wreck, it was really important to me to do what I could and give it my best shot to reach him. However, experiencing depression and sleepless nights at home after having a new baby, left me completely exhausted both mentally and physically. My box was beginning to empty and I didn't think I was capable of pulling out any more tricks. I became weaker and weaker every day. Soon I even struggled to eat small bits of food to keep my energy up. This task became extremely difficult for me, and I began to feel like I was failing both at home and at my job.

It was apparent I had already been acting like a zombie robot at home, but things were starting to get even worse. Not being able to control myself, I began taking things out on my baby. If she cried, I got angry. If I had to feed her, I whined about it. If I had to change her diaper, I griped and complained. The daily tasks and routines of caring for my little girl became overwhelming and daunting. Each passing day without proper nourishment or sleep triggered more depression. It was getting bad, and I didn't know if I would ever be able to get off the ropes.

Though I never actually hurt Macie, I can recount a terrible day when things could have gone south quickly if I hadn't had my family around to intervene. My parents were having a barbeque at their house, and all of my brothers and sisters were there with their spouses and kids. When I arrived at my folks' house, I had Macie in my arms as Scott and Maverick followed behind. I opened the door without knocking, raced straight to the kitchen where my mother and sister were standing, and demanded someone take my baby from me before I hurt her. The nonstop crying had been shattering my eardrums. It had gotten to me so badly I was about to lose every bit of self-control I had. This sweet little baby was just trying to express how she was feeling in the only way she knew how, but I didn't care at the moment. Instead, I handed her off to my sister and shouted desperately, "Get her away from me! I don't want to look at her anymore! Keep her out of my sight!" My sister opened her eyes wide in confusion, looked at me like I was a crazy person (which I was), and took Macie from me right away. Then I stormed out into the backyard to cool off, but I wasn't settling down easily. I continued to be a complete and utter mess. It was clear something was definitely wrong.

Embarrassed by my behavior, I sat down and had a talk with my mom. I cried and told her what a hard time I was having with everything. I mentioned I was concerned about having postpartum depression. My mom did not disagree. She was a wonderful listener and had honest advice. It helped calm my anger and bring me back to reality. By the time the party was ending, I was capable of handling my baby again. Nonetheless, my depression did not quite go away.

It was Monday morning (many weeks after my parent's barbeque), and I had to, once again, go in and face my class surviving on very few hours of sleep. The particular student in my class who I described earlier was not only disobedient, he was aggressive and tried to hurt other kids almost every day. Without the support of his parents, there wasn't a whole lot I was able to do on my own. Then one evening I had a really bad nightmare. I dreamt this boy was beating up one of his classmates, so I grabbed him by the arm and threw him up against the wall, held him by the neck, kept him there for a bit, and warned him never to put his hands on any of my students again. When I woke up the next morning, I remembered the nightmare vividly. It stuck with me all day long and was very disturbing. I would never, ever intentionally hurt a child, though this boy's behavior was getting out of hand. I started getting nervous wondering if I would grab his arm or do something on impulse to keep him from hurting someone else, like I did in my nightmare.

One day, my class was watching a science film, and the boy in question was sitting on the rug, nicely at first. Then all of a sudden, he leaned over to one of his classmates and smacked the boy's head into a metal cart against the wall. I called the office immediately for help, and the other child who was hurt went up to the office to get ice. I felt bad and quite helpless, and those feelings weighed on me heavily. I was honest with my principal and explained to him that I was exhausted and totally stressed out. It was clear I hadn't been eating or sleeping properly. I also admitted I was nearly fainting many times during the day. Things would go black in front of me often, but I never passed out completely. My principal offered to help and do the best he could with my situation, as my health was quickly spiraling downhill. Talk about feeling like you've been boxed into a corner. It felt as though the corner I was boxed into had a deep, wide hole with no way out. I certainly was feeling defeated.

Round 7

THROWING IN THE TOWEL

Four days had gone by when I hadn't slept at all. I was beginning to lose my mind. It was obvious I had to do something about this before I accidentally hurt my baby or someone else. So, trying to do the right thing, I called for a substitute teacher and made an appointment with my doctor.

It was Thursday morning when I went in to see my doctor. He asked me why I was there, and I explained to him that I had lost a ton of weight, hadn't been able to eat or sleep, was feeling depressed, and was beginning to have some fainting spells. All I asked him for was to give me a week or two off work so I could sleep, try to eat, and regain my strength. I also mentioned I thought I had been experiencing postpartum depression for a while now and things had been getting much worse.

The doctor (who was no Dr. Berberich by any standard) responded as if my symptoms were not a big deal. He refused to give me even one day off work to rest. He didn't even recommend I go see a counselor or a psychiatrist. Here I was, skinny and malnourished, lethargic, depressed, and desperately seeking some kind of help from my doctor. Do you know what his only advice to me was? He said, "We have a stress class on Saturdays you can attend." What I really wanted to say to him was, "Are you f-cking kidding me? A stress class once a week? Do you think I look like I am in any shape or form right now to be able to attend a stress class? I couldn't even drive myself here today. I am a serious wreck! My god, why won't you help me?" However, I didn't say any of that because I was too weak (both mentally and physically). Instead, I just cried and begged him to give me a little time off work so I could sleep and get myself straight again. He continued to turn down my request, actually apologizing about it. *Why even try to apologize? You clearly don't give a rat's ass about me right now.*

It was useless to continue pleading my case, as I was obviously not getting anywhere with him. All he would offer me was that damn stress class on Saturday. If things had actually gone awry (as they nearly did), I wouldn't have even been alive on Saturday to show up to the class. There was no way I could function another day like this, and going to a stress class once a week was not a reasonable solution for what I was going through. Either he didn't believe in such a thing as postpartum depression (or any other form of depression for that matter, because all the signs were there), or he really didn't have the patience for crying women. It's still completely inconceivable to me he didn't refer me over to mental health since he had very little to offer on his own. Whatever the case, he certainly failed me that day because I left his office feeling hopeless and suicidal. I had most assuredly thrown in the towel.

When I arrived home, I was an absolute trainwreck. I couldn't believe there wasn't any real help for my situation. I Immediately began having suicidal thoughts. What was the point of living if every day was going to be as dark as it had been for months with no hope of getting any real professional help? Being more than exhausted from only having slept a couple hours in the last four days in a row, I began to have a serious meltdown. I was completely losing my mind. People can die from not getting enough sleep. I read somewhere that soldiers in the field can only go without sleep for 72 hours, otherwise they will have a difficult time both mentally and physically completing their expected tasks. I was certainly no soldier in the toughness department, and I had gone well beyond 72 hours with only a couple hours of sleep to my name.

Beyond all the physical symptoms which occur from a lack of sleep, major cognitive issues can arise as well. That is exactly what ended up happening to me. While this is a humiliating thing to admit, I think it is important for people to understand what can happen to your brain with an immense amount of sleep deprivation and depression. During this time, I ended up having what I believe to be a psychotic episode. I remember sitting on my couch and seeing an arm in front of me that looked like mine, but I knew it wasn't the real thing. It was in black and white like old-time photos or movies. Next, a silver, jagged knife with a black handle appeared above and slowly traced down the arm, cutting the skin just enough to draw a drop of blood. The image in my hallucination reminded me of the movie *American Psycho*. The main actor, Christian Bale, was portrayed romanticizing beautiful images in his mind instead of seeing the actual gore he created in reality. My brain envisioned the same type of violent scene in a beautiful, peaceful way as well. The knife stabbing the skin caused no pain and created a perfectly shaped teardrop of blood which was a bright, magnificent color of red. It was similar to the famous red flower petals on the cover poster for the movie *American Beauty*. What it most reminded me of was the black and white pictures with only a small portion of red or pink added to them, making the vibrant color truly stand out. My mind was mesmerized by the illusion of the glamorous drop of blood dripping down the arm in slow motion. It was just like watching a fascinating, dazzling, enchanting film, except in reality it was totally psychotic.

In addition to the psychotic episode, later in the day I felt as if I was having an out-of-body experience. I saw myself floating but knew I wasn't dead. I could see myself walking to the medicine cabinet, but I couldn't feel my body moving to get there. Inside the cabinet were many bottles of pharmaceutical and over-the-counter drugs. I can remember picking each one up and looking at the labels attempting to find one that would allow me to go numb and sleep for several days. Even though I had suicidal thoughts and felt like I wanted to die, I don't believe it was a true attempt at suicide. The scary part is that it certainly could have escalated by accident. My thoughts were mostly of wanting to escape the world for a while, not wanting to see or talk to anyone. The only real way to describe it is similar to wanting to be in a coma for a bit. I didn't want to have the finality of death, but I didn't want to be alive at the moment either. It is a terrible thing to say and admit, but I was definitely not of sound mind when I was going through this. It was a horrible place to be.

The labels I was trying to read on the medicine bottles were completely blurry, even with my excellent eyesight, which makes perfect sense considering the state I was in. I was delusional at that point. While I don't recall which pills or how many I took, I do remember waking up in my son's bed (not having a clue how I got there), where I was curled up looking at my parents who were standing over me. Their faces appeared fuzzy, and their voices were unclear as well. My parents were in my house because my husband was at work, and I had apparently left an alarming message on my mother's phone when I was feeling suicidal.

Not knowing what was really going on, my parents both rushed over to my house and let themselves in. There were only two people in the room, though it was as if hundreds of people were all speaking at the same time. It was the kind of sound you hear when someone tries to talk under water. Their voices were muffled. It was difficult to make out what they were saying at first. Eventually, things became slightly clearer and my mom told me she would help take me to an appointment with the psychiatrist the next day. *Thank you, Mom!* Luckily, I did not have to get a referral from my doctor first.

After finally getting some sleep I desperately needed, my amazing mother came and picked me up so I wouldn't have to drive alone to the hospital. My husband was more than willing to help me as well, but I wanted him to be able to go to work. Plus, mothers have their own unique way of being a comforting support, which is different from a spouse. They are both wonderful supportive people in my life. It was just nice to have my mom along with me that day.

This time, thankfully, I was able to meet with a psychiatrist. I explained my situation, telling her the exact same things I had told my other doctor the day before. I had lost a lot of weight, was unable to sleep, felt weak, faint, helpless, and confused. I honestly thought if I didn't take a break from work to get healthy, I would impulsively do something stupid and get myself fired. When I sheepishly explained to the psychiatrist that I thought I had postpartum depression, she didn't bat an eye. Instead, she listened to me intently and said she wanted me to take at least a couple weeks off from work to start. Then she would meet with me again to see how I was doing and reevaluate my situation. She also asked me several questions alluding to suicidal tendencies. I explained to her that while I had suicidal thoughts, it was never my true intention to kill myself. The mental and physical exhaustion that had taken over my mind and body had me already feeling as close to dead as one could be. Fortunately, it didn't have my soul. What I really wanted was just to go numb, sleep, and escape real life for a while until I could find hope again.

After studying me closely, the doctor asked who would be looking after me during this time. Then she questioned the scab on my left arm. At first, I was confused, then I looked over at my arm and saw the mark she was referring to. It appeared my hallucination was somewhat real. I don't know how, and I honestly couldn't remember holding anything sharp. She wisely did not feel it was safe for me to be left alone yet. Fortunately, my mother had been sitting in the waiting room, so I invited her in to speak with the doctor. My mom reassured her she would not be leaving me alone. If it wasn't for my remarkable mother, the doctor said she would have hospitalized me. While I understand the reasoning behind it, being put in the hospital would have undoubtedly torn me apart. I'm beyond thankful my mom was there to save me that day.

I left the hospital this time feeling quite relieved. At least I had been heard, understood, and was getting some help to support this illness. Along with seeing the psychiatrist who could prescribe some sleep and antidepressant medication for me, I had weekly appointments with two different counselors as well. One was an incredible man with an adorable accent, who I eventually formed a trusting bond with. The other counselor (who mainly practiced EMDR with me) was a tiny, older woman from the Philippines who was an absolute spitfire. She was sassy and hysterical. They both turned out to be incredible doctors for me, and I looked forward to the time I got to spend with each of them. Unfortunately, 30 minutes once a week was not nearly enough to cure my depression. I feel I would have benefited from daily interventions instead.

I was happy the doctors in the mental health department were actually listening to me since postpartum depression initially seems frequently misjudged. Even the famous Tom Cruise once publicly ridiculed Brooke Shields for being "irresponsible" for supporting antidepressants to help her illness which she discussed in her book *Down Came the Rain*. It really shouldn't matter how people choose to get over their depression as long as they are able to heal. Otherwise, much worse scenarios are bound to occur. I personally bought and read Brooke Shield's book so I would not feel like the only one going through this type of depression. She was courageous in opening up about her own battles with postpartum depression. I imagine it wasn't easy for a well-known actor like her to come out and admit she was in a dark place. Aren't most of us used to celebrities showing us the glamorous, fake, perfect side of themselves? Brooke Shields was authentic and raw. I felt she used her celebrity status for good, helping this important and relevant topic to gain the awareness, understanding, and recognition it deserved. Due to her honesty, bravery and resilience, I am fairly certain she was able to support many women who felt the same way she did but were unable to express it themselves. I appreciated being able to get a glimpse of her imperfect life as it was unfolding before her because I could identify with so many of those feelings. It really helped put things in perspective for me. I only wish there could have been more of a solution for me at the time.

I believe Tom Cruise made a mistake by demeaning Brooke Shields in that manner. (I admit it was similar to the way I judged boxers before meeting Roy.) If you have never been a woman or had a baby, you have no reason to pass judgment. That goes for anyone speaking without experience. Yes, I had to learn that lesson too. It's nice that Brooke Shields was able to forgive Mr. Cruise, and though I love all Tom Cruise's films, especially *Top Gun*, I want to be clear I did not name my son Maverick after his character. Instead, he was named after a cowboy who chose to be nonconforming and stand up for what was right. Tom's criticism of Brooke or any other mothers going through postpartum depression was what I would consider to have been the "irresponsible" thing to do. I get it though. I have made mistakes, learned to apologize, and forgive as well. So, I will continue to watch his movies, and of course will have to go see the film *Maverick*. At least it is a damn cool name.

Another story I read about postpartum depression which helped put things into perspective for me was called *The Cradle Will Fall*. It was a heartbreaking story written by Carl S. Burak, MD, JD and Michele G. Remington. This was a true account of how Michele killed her infant son and then turned the gun on herself in an attempt to commit suicide. Michele committed a horrendous crime but "lived" to face the consequences of her actions. Carl Burak was Michele's psychiatrist who worked with her throughout this horrible ordeal. Together, they were able to convince people this type of depression (severe PPD) was real, and she eventually gained understanding and forgiveness from her community. *The Cradle Will Fall*, while tragic and disturbing at times, fortunately had a triumphant ending by revealing the undeniable power postpartum depression can have over women. It is a good story for women to read to comprehend what emotions (or lack thereof) can occur with this type of illness.

Though Michele's postpartum depression ended up being more drastic than mine in the end, I could still identify with a number of relatable moods and feelings. There was a part in the story where Michele's mom came to visit and saw Michele just rocking back and forth with tears falling down her face. Michele's mood felt stoic, and she seemed detached from reality. I knew the feeling all too well. What bothered me most was her mother knew Michele needed help and called a doctor right away only to be pushed aside and not taken seriously. The lady on the other end of the phone did not appear as if she believed the symptoms were dire because there were no physical problems such as pain or bleeding. Even with the way Michele's mom pleaded and reiterated the seriousness of Michele's depression, demanding to at least speak with her doctor, she was still basically ignored and shunned. The lady said Michele's doctor would see her on her scheduled appointment six days from then and remarked, "Don't worry—it's only the baby blues."

The familiarity of her story was devastatingly real to me. Her feelings of extreme sadness, unworthiness, and hopelessness coupled with her experience of trying to reach her doctor were way too similar to my own story. If I had been made to wait six more days after my doctor sent me home not believing there was anything wrong with me, I'm fairly certain I would not be alive today. If someone is that far gone and seriously depressed, it should not be turned into a waiting game, but viewed as an emergency instead. I can only hope doctors and other individuals are starting to see this as an extreme danger to human lives and are taking the precautions and steps necessary to treat the individual appropriately. There are endless ways I can express the crucial need for deep depression to be taken seriously. I can only hope people are out there listening, taking note, and believing it is real.

While reading those books and realizing I wasn't alone definitely helped, I still needed more to pull me out of my depressive state of mind. Along with my lack of mental stability, my physical health was weak as well. Most days I didn't even want to get out of bed, but it wasn't an option. I still had a family I was responsible for. I was aware I was not doing a good job, but it was all I had to give at that moment. A lot needed to change before I would be healthy again.

Sadly, but not surprisingly given the situation, I had isolated myself away from the world. When my friends called, I refused to answer the phone or return their messages. Eventually many of them just gave up. Nobody knew how bad my depression had gotten because I wouldn't bother talking to anyone about it. Instead, I just stayed in my little hole of darkness and hid myself away from everyone for as long as I could. I allowed my depression and anxiety to continue to weaken me until the day I pulled out those special boxing gloves gifted to me by the wonderful Roy Jones Jr. That was the true turning point which snapped me out of the most wicked depression I had ever experienced.

Round 8

COME OUT SWINGING

Despite trying many different things to help me overcome my anxiety and depression in the past, it didn't seem there was an easy fix or solution to my current problems. I could never quite get the confidence and relief I needed. Nothing I had done before came close to the mental and physical strength, boost of energy, and self-esteem I started to gain from boxing.

When I first found the boxing gloves Roy had given me, I was still in a very deep, dark state of depression. I was super weak, had minimal energy, and my head felt cloudy and confused. Going out in public was tough for me. If someone in a store asked me a question, I would struggle to answer properly with a complete sentence. I also constantly feared becoming tongue-tied or saying something that didn't make sense. My head regularly felt dazed and discombobulated.

Though I was very good in school, always earning great grades, I started to feel awkwardly dumb. How could this be? I graduated from high school, went to college, earned a bachelor's degree, and then went on to earn a master's degree. I certainly wasn't unintelligent, so how could it be so difficult for me to answer a simple question or form a proper sentence? Once someone explained to me why I had been having those issues, it began to make perfect sense. The constant feeling of confusion and inability to speak at times was caused from a lack of sleep, anxiety, depression, and not getting enough oxygen to the brain. Poor mental or physical health can have such a dramatic effect on your mind, body, and soul, so those were the things I needed to begin focusing on. I had to start taking care of me before I would be strong enough to properly take care of anyone else.

To fix my mental and physical state, there was no other choice but to come out swinging. I had to prepare for the fight. At this point, I was ready and willing to make a change, and the boxing gloves Roy gifted me were a wonderful inspiration. They were exactly what I needed to begin to pull myself out of the terrible depression I was in.

Due to my current state of health, it was important to start out slow, not that I had much of a choice. So, I began with putting the boxing gloves on my hands, standing up (which I hadn't done much of since I was always cocooned in my blanket on the couch), and doing a little shadow boxing. Often times, I was a bit lazy and would sit on the couch pretending to punch people on the TV screen. At least it gave me something to focus on. It was also a good way to keep part of my body moving when I was too tired to stand. To be honest, I did kind of enjoy trying to punch certain people on the television screen who rubbed me the wrong way. It made me laugh.

Shadow boxing was pretty fun and could easily be done anywhere. Having a mirror to look in was not essential. It wasn't as much about proper form at this point, but more about just getting my body moving. Plus, it was uplifting. I liked using the gloves to punch. Sometimes I would even throw in a few kicks when I felt bold enough to try. I wished it would have been as easy as going out to play tennis, soccer, or softball—the sports I was already good at. However, being responsible for little ones made it much more difficult to find the time to play a team sport, which was another reason boxing worked so well for me. It was a sport that afforded me the exercise I needed and could do at my own house any time it was convenient.

With having a baby and a toddler to care for, boxing was the absolute best choice. I attempted yoga a few times, but it never really resonated with me. Since I grew up playing sports with guys most of my life, I was used to hitting, kicking, or throwing something. With boxing, I got at least one out of three. Actually, that would make three out of three if you consider "throwing" punches and "kick" boxing. Plus, the mental focus and concentration was intense when I hit the punching bag. Boxing helped fulfill the exercise my body required, the focus my mind craved, and the balance my soul needed. My spirits were lifting, and I was conquering the depression. Boxing was producing a winning outcome for me.

It took several days of merely shadowboxing around my house since it was all the strength I could muster at first. Being able to do only that and turn on some upbeat music already made a huge impact. I'm not going to lie—getting my body moving was extremely challenging after I had practically been hibernating for so long. I hadn't been exercising at all. Depression had a way of literally keeping me down. I found shadowboxing to be such an easy, exhilarating way to begin.

After purely just shadowboxing for a while, I began to feel like I was ready for more. Next, I moved onto the punching bag. I didn't use the thick, massive bag that hangs from the ceiling. Instead, I preferred the little punching bag which came on a stand. This was the one where you punch it, it goes flying, and then comes right back toward you pretty damn fast. It was liberating to feel and watch the bag fly back when I hit it. I had to use focus and concentration to hit it every time it came back without missing. The speed was quick, so I really had to pay attention and be ready to move at a swift pace. It was great exercise, really helped strengthen my muscles, and absolutely nourished my brain.

On a separate note, this could be an incredibly helpful exercise to use beyond just conquering depression. If you are upset or angry (or have terrible PMS like I did before children), it can be quite a fun and beneficial tool for you to get your frustrations out. This might sound a bit ruthless, but I promise you it is not intended that way. None of us are perfect beings, and we all get hurt or upset from time to time. Plus, I haven't come across too many females who are experts at controlling those little nuisances we have within our bodies called "hormones." So, this can be a more positive way to deal best with those beastly issues. You better believe I am going to teach this strategy to my daughter when she hits those teenage years.

Let's say you come home and are resentful, annoyed, or enraged over something someone said or did to you. Think about the person and instead of letting them continue to infuriate you, put on your gloves, go out to your bag, and picture punching them in the face. I use the face as an example, but you may choose a different body part (especially if it is an ex of yours). You could even pin or tape up a picture if you wanted to. I know, it sounds both vicious and funny at the same time, but it honestly works.

Rather than remaining angry and letting it affect you, get your feelings out with exercise and laughter. Laughter is great medicine, and if you cannot giggle while pretending to punch your antagonizer in the face or elsewhere, then I don't know what to tell you. It absolutely worked for me. Then I could never truly stay angry at the person because I secretly could visualize what I did. Nobody has to get hurt this way, and there's no harm done when you are doing this at your own home with only your imagination. No matter who upset you, this is a positive way to handle it without wallowing in the stress. I found this technique to be quite beneficial, and better than yoga or meditation for me in those types of circumstances. It was great to release anger and frustration without anyone having to get hurt in the process.

Once I had built up enough energy and strength from the shadowboxing I learned from Roy and also by punching my bag, I decided to try out some weights. Again, I was coming from a weakened state, so I had to start easy. I began lifting little three-pound dumbbells and working my boxing punches with them in slow motion. I used a series of movements called jabs, hooks, uppercuts, and crosses. After practicing those moves with the weights, I would put the dumbbells down and repeat the same movements with my bare fists as fast as I could. It was an exhilarating feeling!

My depression and blues had slowly started to dissolve once I began this simple boxing routine. One of its great advantages compared to other workout routines was that it didn't cost much money. Not only did I not have to buy a gym membership, but the equipment was extremely affordable. The punching bag was around $30, a set of dumbbells was around the same, and a decent pair of boxing gloves (which I luckily didn't have to purchase) could be bought for under $30 as well. I've also noticed many companies who make boxing gloves have added some pretty colors for women now too (or men—no discriminating here). Looking at beautiful, vibrant colors can definitely be a plus when you need to feel better. During massage school, I studied color therapy. There really is something special and healing about the colors we choose to wear or have around us for different reasons.

What is also great about boxing at home is not having to wear fancy outfits. Bright colors can definitely help boost energy. However, it isn't necessary to have the most impressive or expensive outfits or high-end training equipment to get healthy. You simply need a reason and a little inspiration to get you going.

While putting on those fun, bright red boxing gloves was my initial inspiration, getting healthy for my family truly was my reason. I had a choice. Either I could wallow in my sorrow and let the depression overtake me for good, or I could choose to do something about it. I chose to stand up and fight for my health and my family.

Happily, the boxing routine worked for me. It has been better than anything I have ever tried. I admit I haven't always done it regularly since I began to use boxing after my postpartum depression. There have been times I would get busy and not even exercise at all. Again, I am far from perfect. I have even had other bouts of depression. Things happen in life that are out of our control, whether it's work stress, life issues, grief, or something else. We all know life is a roller coaster. However, when I have found myself struggling with anxiety or depression again, I at least have the tools to work on it. The hardest part is realizing it and then admitting you are in a funk. Then you have to determine what you are willing to do to make a change and get out of that negative headspace. Hopefully, in the way I have, you choose to be heathy, positive, and happy.

Round 9

GOING THE DISTANCE

After I had found the boxing gloves Roy had given me and started exercising a bit, I realized I truly did want to focus on becoming a fighter. Though, I meant it in the way you work hard for what you want to accomplish, stand up for what you believe in, advocate for your own health, and don't give into failure or give up on things you feel passionate about. I didn't want to get into a ring like Roy and try to destroy my opponent. I just wanted the meaning of fighting to help me feel stronger and more confident in life. I was ready and willing to start working harder and go the distance.

Once I was back on my feet and feeling better about myself, I got up the courage to put in a call to Roy. I wanted to prove I could be a fighter and overcome all of this. It would have been easy to continue with my basic boxing routine I had managed to put together from bits of Roy's previous lessons and knowledge from my own experience with sports. Yet, I wanted to dive in deeper. I needed to come out of this feeling exceptionally strong so I would have the tools to climb my way out of the hole if I ever fell deep into one again. Since Roy was a professional, he would know how to push me to reach the level of success I wanted to achieve. Knowing it would not be an easy task was one of the reasons I wanted to do it.

Initially, it wasn't that I felt scared to ask Roy for help. Instead, it was the fear of humiliating myself by admitting to him what I had gone through. Here was a world champion athlete who was as mentally and physically strong as the best of the best. Then there was me. While I was a strong athlete in many sports, I still was never a pro. At this point in my life, I wouldn't even say I was athletic anymore. I was barely hanging on. Roy and others knew me as healthy and fit with a powerful and sassy attitude. Seeing me that way now would merely be an illusion. And though no one expected me to, I was embarrassed about not being strong enough to conquer this on my own. On the outside, I liked to act as if I were tough, but on the inside I felt weak. There were definitely moments throughout my life when I felt strong and confident, but there were times when I was absolutely broken. This was one of those times, and the strength was only going to come from being vulnerable and admitting the truth. I really could not do this alone.

Asking for help is truly one of the hardest things to do. Why is it so challenging and difficult? Successful people don't usually get there alone. We all know you can accomplish more with a team or the assistance of others. Doing things alone takes so much more time and energy. So, why is it that hard for us to ask? I guess you could call it ego. We should be smart enough and confident enough to do things on our own, right? It isn't always as simple. Personally, I believe the smartest ones are those who know how to ask for help when they need it, then they move forward instead of being stuck. Realizing this, I finally mustered up the courage to be vulnerable and ask for the kind of help I felt I needed.

When I dialed Roy this time, I was far from my usual mouthy self. Alternately, I was humbled and feeling a bit sensitive as I opened myself up and explained my situation. What I wanted was to move forward and never look back. Since I needed to become a fighter, I asked Roy if he would train me and give me something to push me beyond my limits.

I was eternally grateful when Roy accepted my proposal. He was as kind and generous as could be. There are so many unique facets to Roy's personality, though being a helpful and caring human being truly makes him a hero in my book. Not once did he make me feel ashamed or stupid for my behavior and the depression I was going through. If I fought back with an "I can't" attitude, he didn't scold me. Instead, he just pushed me to move forward so I wouldn't shut down.

Roy was fantastic at encouraging me and didn't reprimand me for sometimes needing to go at a slower pace. He did laugh at me, but I laughed at myself too. I can admit I am not always the easiest at taking direction, but I never want to let anybody down. So while I might have been a slight pain in the ass, I was still willing to get the job done.

With Roy living all the way across the country in Florida while I resided in California, it was difficult to do all the trainings in person. We managed by doing as much as we could over the phone. When Roy had a job out here in Los Angeles, I was able to meet up with him to get a better idea of how to perform the boxing movements.

Beginning the training was unbelievably tough on me. Roy said it was important to work on my endurance first. He expected me to run at least three miles at the beginning and increase the number each week. *No problem*, I initially thought. I did this all the time when I played varsity soccer in high school. Not long after I began running, I embarrassingly had to come to the sad realization I was not in high school anymore, nor was my body in the same shape. Sister Kara, on the other hand, was still an avid runner who also played soccer in college. To this day, she continues to compete in the Ragnar run every year and tries to do partial marathons when she can. So I figured I would get her to help me run, and it would be a great bonding experience for us.

To begin my endurance training, Kara met me at my house. We had our sexy running outfits on, makeup done to a T, and our hair curled perfectly and pinned up just so. Jokes aside, we wore fairly unattractive workout clothes, no makeup, sunscreen, and our hair tied back in ugly, sweaty ponytails. We set off on our running adventure, and I was happily jogging along at my baby sister's pace. Then we got about a mile into the run when I asked her if she would mind slowing down just a tad. She laughed at me, of course, but did as I asked or I wouldn't have been able to keep up. As we continued, my back started to sting and my knees began to feel sore. My god, I was out of shape. Getting older sucked, and obviously my body wasn't the same after having a couple of babies. That was no excuse, though, and I knew I had to continue despite the pain.

We finished the run—well, at least Kara did. I had to walk the last little bit. It was my first time out and I was unbelievably out of shape. I made it back without anyone having to come pick me up, so that was a decent accomplishment. My nice sister was super encouraging to me as I slowly huffed and puffed behind her. Distance running was no joke. I preferred the shorter, faster sprints rather than jogging for miles. It didn't matter though. I had to do what my coach told me.

Another exercise Roy encouraged me to do was to jump rope. He said to start off with five minutes and increase the time as I went. Jumping rope was going to be so much fun, I just knew it. I could remember loving it as a kid. The many twists, skips, figure eights, and other cool moves I could do with the jump rope were going to come right back to me as easy as riding a bike. They didn't—I was wrong, way wrong. Jumping rope was unbelievably hard! I wasn't lightly bouncing up and down with springs in my feet like I remember doing as a child. In fact, I barely lasted an entire 60 seconds let alone five minutes. Though I was fairly petite at the time, it felt as if I was carrying the weight of an elephant landing hard on the ground with a giant thud after every jump.

Oh my gosh, I didn't recall jump-roping being such a discouraging and painful ordeal. I was sweating like a dog and feverishly watching the seconds go by on the timer. *Holy crap!* I thought. Were these five obnoxiously painful minutes ever going to end? It felt like pure torture. I know, I was such a whiner. It was way harder than I had imagined and not at all like the experiences I had as a child jumping rope, like the amazing Double Dutch. Too bad I couldn't have jumped rope on a bouncy trampoline for a while. It was seriously more challenging than I remembered it being.

While working on endurance, Roy also had instructions for me regarding healthy eating. I wasn't initially aware this would be part of the training. Damn! When Roy told me to cut out sugar, I think my mouth dropped wide open and hit the floor. "You just mean the white sugar, right? I'm still allowed to eat the brown kind, aren't I?" I asked nicely hoping he would give in. "No brown sugar? How about the powdered kind then?" I playfully asked. "You know, it won't feel like a proper Sunday morning without homemade waffles with butter, warm maple syrup, and lots of delicious powdered sugar sprinkled on top." Unfortunately, I wasn't getting anywhere with my attempt at being cute. This was going to be trickier than I thought.

Next, I began to worry about my favorite food of all time. "Um, I'm sorry Roy, but I don't know of any sugar-free types of ice cream (that I would actually consider putting in my mouth). Are you serious? Do I really have to cut out sugar?" I asked him. He always said "yes," of course. "Oh my gosh, I don't have a clue what to eat," I explained. "Can you please give me some examples of healthy choices I can consume without gagging?" I asked. Roy told me to eat raw foods like fruits, vegetables, beans, nuts, and grains. This was the part where I got a little feisty. I said, "I eat Mexican food nearly three times a day. I could practically live on flour tortillas and butter alone. I absolutely must have some type of chocolate occasionally (I really meant often), or I might hurt somebody. Now what is it exactly you expect me to eat again? Somehow, I have a feeling refried beans were probably not the type of beans you were referring to." Roy just laughed as if I was pulling his leg. I wasn't. I was totally serious. I had never eaten that unbelievably healthy in my life. I wondered how I was ever going to get through this.

Roy was very serious about me changing my eating habits for our training purposes. If I was going to do this right, then I needed to eat right as well. I acted as if I completely understood what he was asking of me. However, I may have skirted around this subject a bit. Honestly, I tried to improve my diet, but I admittedly did not hold up to the standards Roy wanted me to. I cheated... a lot. While I truly concentrated a hundred percent on his fitness training advice, I wasn't perfect with the food challenge. This was all okay because it helped me admit and come to terms with my faults. After all, I needed to leave room to improve something, right?

To be honest, being that hardcore about my diet wasn't something I couldn't do, it was something I wasn't willing to do. Let me explain. I was someone who grew up with poor self-esteem and constantly used the word "can't." It was even written on one of my report cards. The teacher specifically wrote, "Amy needs to stop saying 'I can't.' She is very smart and capable of doing many things." Unfortunately, it didn't stop me. I continued using the words into adulthood. Then I read a book my sister gave to me which changed my way of thinking. The book was called *Unfu*k Yourself,* by Gary John Bishop. Anything with that word in it, I typically found hysterical and intriguing. The F-word could be extremely powerful or hilarious when used in the right context. One of the key points mentioned in the book was, "What are you willing or unwilling to do in order to change your life?" I used that particular question to help change my brain. I thought, *Instead of saying I can't, I am going to ask myself, are you willing or* *unwilling to do it?* This simple, reflective question completely changed my way of thinking.

Thanks to Bishop's book, I came up with an idea for my class, to teach my students not to use the words "I can't" either. My sister-in-law Kathy is a super talented artist. She was a graphic designer for over twenty years but has many other talents. She even built a remarkable tree house that could have been featured on one of the popular shows like *Treehouse Masters*. It was that good. There isn't anything Kathy can't do, so I gave her the task of designing several shirts for me that simply said, "I will..." These were easy for Kathy to make, and we had fun playing around with several fonts and colors.

After the shirts were finished, I wore one to school each day and worked on a different skill with my class. Various skills included raising their hand to talk, pushing in their chair, completing an activity, and complimenting a friend. The students would earn extra points for demonstrating the rule or social skill I asked them to do each day. For example, we would always begin with, "I will...stand quietly in line." If any of my students said, "I can't do this," I would simply point to the words on my shirt and ask, "But are you *willing* to do it?" That always stopped them in their tracks, and they would immediately try to do the thing they were originally saying they couldn't do. Using the phrase, "I will..." has made a big impact on my students since I began doing it several years ago. I have gotten fairly good at remembering to use the phrase myself (most of the time). However, my point is while I was willing to do the physical training with Roy, I was unwilling to give up certain foods. At least I never said, "No or I can't," right? Honestly, I did a decent job with my diet. It was important to take all of Roy's training advice seriously. If I had to name an area I know I struggled in or could have improved upon, that would have been it.

Meanwhile, I felt like my endurance training with Roy was going really well so far. I had a lot more stamina and was feeling good physically. Next, it was time to add in some strength training. Roy had me incorporate weights into my workout routine. Slowly but surely, I began doing repetitions with the dumbbells.

When I first started out, during my own training, I was only able to lift three pounds. Yes, I was still very weak in the muscle department, so it was a big deal to me when I was able to move up to a whole five-pound dumbbell. I know it probably sounds like a sissy weight for many, but it was a big improvement from my original state of weakness. Along with the free weights, I built strength by doing push-ups, sit-ups, bicycle kicks, flutter kicks, leg raises, side scissors, and walking lunges. This point in the training was still all fitness based. Roy would not allow me to put on the gloves yet. I had to earn those little magical red rays of sunshine. The moment I would slide them over my hands created a positive shift of energy I could feel throughout my entire body. No other inanimate object gave me the same sense of energy, power, and uplifting spirit. When I put the gloves on, it was like an animated show where you would see immediate glitter or sparkles flying all around. I wasn't hallucinating those times, I promise. It was just the incredible feeling I would get from putting the special gloves on.

At last, Roy let me know he was going to be coming out to L.A. to work as a commentator for a big fight. I was so excited to finally get in some real boxing training, back to my favorite jabs, crosses, bobs and weaves, ducks, and blocks. Plus, Roy made a much better and a lot more fun punching bag than the one I had at home. Though he was a bit older now than when I punched him in his prime, I still figured I would get hurt before he would. It wasn't even a contest.

Roy and I met up at a premiere hotel in L.A. right after the fight was over. Hanging out in public was a bit of a chore for Roy. As with any celebrity, people stared and wanted his attention, pictures, and autographs. Understanding what comes with fame, Roy obliged his fans when he could. He was a really good sport about it all.

We tried to walk over to an inconspicuous area away from the lobby and bar where we could focus on more of the boxing techniques. Roy graciously showed me how to throw some different types of punches as I made a tight fist and aimed for his open hands. Once again, he laughed at my pathetic attempt to punch him as I started off being quite reserved. The more he taunted and teased me, the harder I punched. It was all in good fun. He described the different stances and techniques we were focusing on, which to be honest, went completely over my head at first. Then I began to understand what he was telling me, and I started to pick up momentum. As always, I got a kick out of fighting with the legend. He left me with plenty of boxing techniques and strategies to practice and work on over the weeks and months to come. After my lesson was over, I thanked Roy profusely and began to gather my items to begin heading home.

I used everything Roy had taught me and continued to train as hard as I could. It was important to me to stay healthy and remain in great shape. No way did I want to return to the sad place I had been in before. Roy and I kept up on the phone since he lived so far away, but it was mainly just to report how I was doing with it all. I was happy to say I was doing really well for a while with all he had taught me.

Round 10

HIT BELOW THE BELT

After training with Roy for a bit, I was in really great shape. Unfortunately, being in good shape didn't mean health issues couldn't arise. I believed I was more capable of dealing with them due to my training though. I didn't know what was going on exactly, but I informed Roy I might be M.I.A. for a little bit while I figured it out and attempted to handle the problem.

Being in pain and discomfort is no way to live, so I finally decided it was time to go see a doctor. This one was no better than the doctor I had originally seen to address my postpartum depression. I had been experiencing a lot of stomach pain, and he simply wanted to diagnose me with irritable bowel syndrome (IBS) and call it a day. My opinion was the term IBS was "bullshit" for "I don't actually know what is wrong with you, so I'm just going to call it IBS." It simply meant, "I am BSing you." I didn't have freaking IBS! My bowels were wonderful, and I was proud of the way I eliminated my food, to put it the classiest way I could. And I didn't have acid reflux either. The doctor made me take Prilosec for it anyway, which only made me feel worse. Then of course I began to have depression again because my physical symptoms were not being handled, and I was constantly in pain. This again proved that physical health could affect one's mental well-being and vice versa. I was utterly miserable. My stomach pain was preventing me from being able to handle normal daily activities. I honestly felt as though I had been hit below the belt in more ways than one.

From the beginning, I was certain there was a problem with my gallbladder. I pointed it out to the doctor, but because there weren't any stones on my ultrasound, he refused to believe it was the problem. I literally had to fight for myself. The doctor was planning to leave my diagnosis as IBS and not doing anything else to help me. I pushed to see a gastrointestinal specialist and was able to get an endoscopy. There were a couple more tests administered as well, thank goodness. One of the exams the specialist recommended I have done was a gallbladder function test. As miserable as it was lying perfectly still in a giant tube for two hours, it ended up being worth it. That was it—I knew it! I felt like it was my gallbladder all along. Had I just listened to the doctor and quit pushing to find an answer, I might still have been living with that pain. Once I had the surgery to remove my gallbladder, I felt as good as new. I'm telling you, I have seriously had to learn to become a fighter. It's so important to push some of these doctors and fight for your health. My advice is to be your own advocate because nobody knows your body like you do.

After the gallbladder pain was resolved, I had another more serious health issue a bit later on. I do my annual due diligence and make sure I get a mammogram. A few days after one of them, I was notified that some calcifications were found. While the nurse attempted to assure me that calcifications weren't usually anything to worry about, they still wanted to do a biopsy to make sure everything checked out okay. For obvious reasons, I was not excited to go have a biopsy of my breast done. However, I complied as one should.

When I walked into the room where the biopsies were done, I saw a funky-looking table with two holes in it. Guess what those holes were for? You guessed it. I had never seen a table like it before. All of a sudden, I felt like I was in a Frankenstein movie about to be operated on in a precarious way. I will admit, I started to feel quite nervous and a bit queasy about this procedure. I'll refrain from describing the details other than to say it was notably an awful, uncomfortable experience and not one of my fondest memories.

As if the biopsy wasn't bad enough on its own, I ended up getting a terrible infection from it. Days after the procedure, my breast began to swell, burn, and rash. When I went to the doctor to get it checked out, he treated me for a staph infection with an antibiotic called Bactrim. This unfortunately did not work for me, so I had to have a needle aspiration done, which was unforgivably torturous. Not only did I have to endure this awful procedure once, but I had to start having the needle aspiration about every other day. The fluid inside my breast kept coming back, and the burning infection would not dissipate on its own.

The doctor who was in charge of my procedure was incredibly skilled but was lacking a bit in the commonsense department. I was already a nervous wreck having to lie there with my arm over my head, trying my best to hold still, while having to endure the pain of an enormously big needle being stuck into my breast. That was absolutely miserable. And to make matters even worse, the doctor thought he was a comedian or something. His calm, bedside manner was nonexistent. I'm all one for fun and jokes, but what I was being subjected to was not a laughing matter. This particular doctor was seriously laughing and shouting, "Oh wow, you should see how much puss came out this time! There's an unbelievable amount here! This is unreal! You've got to see this!" He acted like he was really impressed with himself. Without asking me if I "wanted" to look at the disgusting liquid that was just pulled out of my burning, aching breast, he shoved the needle and tube in front of my face before I could answer or have the chance to look away. Needless to say, I did not feel the same excitement he did. It horrified me even more realizing how giant the needle was that had just been stuck in a personal part of my body, and the image of the grotesque fluid was absolutely repulsive. I really just wanted to vomit and get out of that place as fast as I could.

I didn't have to go back and get another needle aspiration after that last horrifying appointment, but it wasn't because he got enough puss out that time. Instead, either the staph infection had gotten worse, or my body's allergic reaction to the antibiotics caused pain and discomfort to spread throughout my body. Believe it or not, things became even more intense.

After the biopsy was read, a nurse made an appointment for me to meet with another doctor to discuss the results. I was sitting in the office, waiting for the doctor to come in, when I finally heard a knock at the door. A nice-looking, blond-haired man, who I suspected was the doctor, walked in wearing a white coat. What I didn't know at the time was he wasn't only a doctor, he was about to become my surgeon. Luckily, he had a very good disposition and demeanor since I would need extra comfort with what he was about to tell me. The doctor started with, "I have some good news and some bad news. We found something in your biopsy that is a fairly big issue. However, it is not cancer yet." I was completely caught off guard by his statement. I nervously wondered what he meant by "not cancer *yet*." Hearing this did not ease my mind at all.

Next, he told me he had to go see another patient, who had been waiting a long time, and deliver some tough news to him, then he would be back to explain the rest of it to me in detail. *Oh crap!* I thought. Hearing the "C" word and not understanding what it meant made me freak out a bit. I got on the phone while I was in his office and called my friend Adrianna, who still lived next door to the wonderful Mama Dee. (She went only by Dee, but I loved calling her Mama Dee because she was such an awesome mama.)

Adrianna had gone through breast cancer a few years prior and was a huge advocate for other women. She had to have a double mastectomy where they weren't able to save her nipples but tattooed some back on her. Adrianna was very open with what she went through. She even gave talks at the hospital voluntarily in order to help women who were going through the same ordeal. She bravely showed them her scars so women could get a real perspective of what this type of surgery might entail. Adrianna was positive and uplifting, and she helped women realize the scars were a small price to pay compared to the alternative. In addition, Adrianna was one of the founders of a nonprofit organization called "Support Sisterz" which helps to empower and support other survivors of breast cancer.

Adrianna was most definitely the right person to call. I was sitting in the room frightened over what the doctor was going to come back and tell me. Instead of simply reassuring me, Adrianna asked if I wanted her to come to the hospital and be there with me when the doctor delivered the news. Not wanting to bother her, I said I would be okay. Then she pretty much demanded (in the nicest way ever) to come because I didn't have it in me to say, "Yes, it would be great if you dropped what you were doing with your kids and husband to come and help me instead." She hung up immediately, got in her car, and drove to the hospital. She made it there before the doctor had come back to see me. We sat and talked for a few minutes, and Adrianna could see how nervous I was about everything. So, she offered to ask the doctor questions for me since she had been through it already. I honestly wouldn't have known what questions to ask or even think about asking.

When the doctor came in, he sat down and started describing the issue they had found in my breast. He explained how it wasn't cancer but was a marker that shows a high risk of developing cancer in the future. This was something called atypical ductal hyperplasia (ADH), and is classified as a high-risk precursor lesion. The diagnosis was not a relief. It scared me because a friend of mine who I worked with told me she had ADH, which led to ductal carcinoma in situ (DCIS). She ended up having a double mastectomy and other treatments to take care of it. I was indeed more than a little freaked out over this news. However, Adrianna asked the doctor some questions for me about best treatments and alleviated some of my concerns. The decision I had made before leaving the doctor's office was to go with a less invasive lumpectomy procedure for the time being.

Adrianna walked out of the hospital with me, let me know I would be okay, and promised to be there to help me along the way. She was such a good friend and advocate for me during that time. I wish it wasn't the case, but I did have to rely on her quite a bit.

Once again, I ended up having to fight for my health and demand they take action sooner than later. I got push-back from the doctor again regarding how to handle my burning infection. Every day the infection was getting worse and my lumpectomy was scheduled a month out still. I tried to explain how I needed something else done because the pain was becoming unbearable, but the doctor kept pushing me aside.

I can clearly remember the Friday morning after severely suffering all night. The pain had spread from being localized in only one breast to different parts throughout my body. I was aching all over, and my legs and back were killing me. This was something I could simply not handle anymore.

Since my husband was at work, I called up my mom and asked her if she was free to drive me to the emergency room. Ever the amazing mother she was (and still is), she said she would come pick me up right away. When we arrived at the hospital, the pain had become so intense I couldn't even walk, so my mom had to find a wheelchair for me.

I was moaning and groaning as I sat in the waiting room, dying for them to hurry up and call my name. People started staring at me because they could see how much discomfort I was in. It was written all over my face, and I had to do my very best to hold back the tears. The excruciating pain had taken over my entire body and then some.

After the nurses triaged me, they sent me over to the waiting room where the doctor I had been meeting with (the one who was going to perform my surgery) was working. He evaluated me and decided I needed emergency surgery because of the infection and amount of pain I was in. Then he proceeded to apologize and tell me how he had to leave in a few minutes to attend one of his child's special school events. He let me know a different surgeon would be taking care of me. When he started describing the new surgeon, I exclaimed, "I thought that kid was your son! You mean the guy I saw sitting with you in your office is actually a doctor?" He laughed fairly hard when I told him I thought it was his son. "No, he's definitely not my son," the doctor explained with a chuckle. "He's actually an incredible surgeon, and you will be in safe hands with him," the doctor assured me. *Holy moly!* I could not believe it— Doogie Howser was going to be performing surgery on me.

As I was escorted away and began to prep for surgery, in strolled the blond, shaggy-haired skater-surfer dude who could not have been a day older than me. (I was much younger at this time.) Thankfully a family friend worked at this particular hospital, so of course I contacted her immediately to get the scoop on this young'un. When I asked her about the surgeon, she laughed and said that almost everyone has the same initial reaction about him, but he was one of their very best surgeons. Hearing that made me feel much better. I tried to relax and begin to put my trust in him, not that I had much choice at the time since I had to have emergency surgery. But I knew I liked this guy immediately after shaking his hand. He was serious business, but also had a foul mouth and a humorous, witty side. He by far was not the most politically correct doctor you would ever meet, but definitely the most fun. It was easy for me to like and bond with him right away.

My IV was in and the meds were starting to flow. I remember being in the operating room with "Doogie" and a couple of his assistants (who also assured me this young doctor was an incredible surgeon) as loud, funky music started blasting in the room. I was surprised he was playing such loud music while performing surgery, but he and his assistants said he does it all the time. Doogie started smiling, dancing, and said, "You are in good hands. We are going to take good care of you, and you'll be all fixed up in no time. Are you ready?" (He was sweet and actually refrained from cussing in the operating room). I nodded my head yes. As the mask came down over my nose and mouth, everything went black, and I went to sleep immediately. When I woke up, I was lying in the recovery room feeling dizzy and spaced out. The nurse let me know my surgery had taken a bit longer than expected due to the infection, but was now over and had gone very well.

I was moved into the hospital room I was going to stay in for a few days until I recovered. Once I woke up from the anesthesia and things became clearer, I noticed there was a tube sticking out from the side of my breast. The nurse told me it was needed to drain the fluid from the infection. Oh my god, it was absolutely disgusting. Not only did I have this gross tube hanging out of my left boob, I also had a burning, red rash that covered my entire body. My face was so swollen I was almost unrecognizable. This was different from the staph infection I already had. I didn't know how it was possible, but I was feeling even worse. What the heck had happened to me? The surgery had supposedly gone very well. The nurse figured I probably had a different allergic reaction to the pain medication they were giving me through my IV. I was burning so badly, the nurse kept having to bring me cool, icy towels to place all over my body. Make no mistake about it, the suffering was real.

Finally, my surgeon (who actually was a brilliant young surfer-skater dude) came to check in on me. He asked how I was doing, boasted humorously about the fantastic job he did getting the infection out, along with enough tissue from the lumpectomy, and dropped a few F-bombs while he was at it. Apparently, it was a very difficult surgery to do based on what had been happening with my infection. So, I let him brag and cuss all he wanted to. He had every right. Plus, he was adamant about finding the right nurses and people to take care of me from there on out. I could tell how bad he felt for me when he came in and saw the burning, red rash all over my body. It was obvious my young, potty-mouthed doctor really did care about his patients. I even appreciated his (not so politically correct) bedside manner. At least he didn't stick gross things in front of my face that made me want to throw up. He just had a relaxed, different way of communicating.

"Dr. Doogie" was seriously a rock star. A good friend of mine named Meghan had to have a complicated surgery on her abdomen and she had him for her doctor as well. We always talked about how we couldn't believe he was such a good surgeon. This guy would seriously throw on a backpack after work and walk down the halls of the hospital with his skateboard in hand. Knowing him, he probably skated down the halls as well when no one was looking. We laughed at his potty mouth and wondered if he spoke that way to his elderly patients. We could not imagine him speaking to an 80-year-old grandma the same way he spoke to us saying, "Don't worry sweetheart, I'm going to take great f-cking care of you. No need to worry about a goddamn thing, you cute little granny you. I've totally got this shit handled." He was honestly hysterical. No other way to describe this young doctor other than to say Meghan and I thought he was just f-cking rad!

Years later when I had to have a hysterectomy, I demanded Dr. Doogie be a part of it. He wasn't supposed to do those types of surgeries unless he was brought in as an emergency due to complications. I was scared shitless to have this surgery because I knew how tricky it was going to be. It was complicated due to the severity of the scar tissue I endured from both of my cesareans. Thankfully, I found a way to get Doogie involved, so I felt extremely comforted knowing I had the best surgeon there to help me if anything were to go wrong.

Back to my procedure, once I was dismissed from the hospital after recovering from the infection and lumpectomy, I had to set up a meeting with the oncologist since ADH was still considered a high risk for developing cancer. When I met with the oncologist, he gave me a few choices. He told me I could take a drug called Tamoxifen for five years, have a bilateral mastectomy, or basically do nothing and hope to catch things early if anything else were to develop. Tamoxifen was not an option because I needed to stay on birth control pills due to my painful periods and endometriosis. Also, it could have increased the chances of developing cancer in other areas such as my ovaries, which would have been worse. Having another surgery sounded like the most horrific thing in the world after what I had just been through. Therefore, I chose to do nothing and hope to god I didn't end up getting cancer later on.

Another doctor I met with, who specialized in working with breast cancer patients, said he supported my decision. Yet, I still had to be monitored closely and make sure to get my mammograms done every three months. Eventually, I was able to move to six months, followed by yearly mammograms after remaining clear for a few years. As a result of what I went through, I never ever forget to have those yearly mammograms done. While there is nothing sexy about them, they could possibly save your life. I have a few friends who I know put them off because it is inconvenient and uncomfortable. While I get it, I still have to highly recommend being diligent about getting mammograms. There's nothing quite like getting your boobs squished and tossed around like fun, little, stretchy balls of dough. But I cannot say enough about how important it is to be proactive about your health.

Round 11

PUT UP YOUR DUKES

There is definitely something to be said about mind, body, and spirit working together. Whenever I went through the physical health issues, I had trouble with my emotions as well. Depression would always kick back in whenever I was not feeling well physically. This happened after my C-sections, with my cervical cancer battle, gallbladder issue, ADH and infection, and hysterectomy. It never failed—I always became depressed. Sometimes, I didn't have the physical ability to stand up and use my body to box. Instead, I had to get into the mindset of remembering how to fight. It was imperative to push through those dark times because as I often witnessed, there eventually would be light.

During the time I was going through my recovery from the hysterectomy (which took much longer to heal than expected due to the severe amount of scar tissue), I was feeling down and out. Without a doubt, I had the blues. At the same time, my neighbor Sheri, who lived two doors down, was fighting her own battle with breast cancer. We were both pretty darn depressed over our situations. She had also been getting the runaround from doctors the same way I had numerous times before. Sheri was at her wits end and wasn't quite sure how to proceed with her cancer treatment. We spoke for a while about my own knowledge of breast cancer and everything my friend Adrianna had taught me.

After a few discussions, Sheri was determined to have a double mastectomy. Initially, her doctor did not want to do what she was asking. Sheri was tired of arguing, so she was ready to put up her dukes and fight for what she believed was best for her in this situation. She wanted it all to be over in one shot and preferred not to live in fear and anxiety wondering if the cancer would return one day. Sheri made her decision and courageously stuck with it.

While we were sharing different past experiences with each other, I told Sheri about my own personal best healing method that came from boxing. She listened intently and understood how it could be such a major attraction. Not only was I getting healthy physically, but it gave me a fighting attitude to deal with many situations regarding my health. If I hadn't pushed, I simply could have been forgotten about or walked all over. With the type of breast cancer Sheri had, she felt she needed to "fight" for her life and future so the cancer would not return to haunt her.

When her surgeries were over and reconstruction was underway, Sheri began to feel better and much more confident about her outcome and life. She decided to have a party to celebrate her health and thank everyone who had been by her side, helping her along her journey. Since we were neighbors, Sheri walked over to my house before her party and let me know she had something important she wanted me to be a part of and she explained how it meant a lot to her. Sheri's party theme was "fighting cancer." That was a nice way of putting it. Actually, Sheri and I would have said, "Let's kick the f-ck out of cancer's ass!" That was honestly how we both really felt about the dreaded "C" word.

When Sheri reached my house and I opened the door to greet her, she handed me a beautiful, bright pink boxing glove and asked me to sign it for her. She wanted all the individuals who had aided her in this fight to sign the glove as a reminder and a keepsake. Then Sheri surprised me with my own pair of pink boxing gloves and told me she wanted those to be an inspiration to encourage me to finish writing my book.

During our conversations, I had mentioned my story about Roy Jones Jr. and the boxing I had done that helped pull me out of my postpartum depression. It not only helped improve my depressive state, it made a huge difference in my health and literally changed my life. For years, I had about three quarters of my book written and could never seem to find the time or inspiration to finish it. Mostly, I was nervous about being so vulnerable and sharing my story with the world. Yet, deep down I knew the only real way to help other people was by being honest and open about my struggles. Sheri encouraged me and refused to let me quit. Unfortunately, quitting was easy for me, then I didn't have to worry about failure or embarrassment. You can't ever grow or go anywhere if you simply give up. Success comes from learning how to fail and continue on anyway.

Thank goodness my friend did not let me quit. Besides, that was exactly what I was trying to learn from Roy. I couldn't let him down after everything he had worked so hard to teach me. I was learning to become a fighter, not a quitter, so I finally pulled it together and realized what I needed to do. I was determined to finish this book and not allow being scared of how people might judge me affect the outcome. I have basically been preaching about becoming a fighter, so giving up was not an option. I had to fight to finish this book and try to help others like I had originally set out to do.

I am very thankful for Sheri. She was there for me when I needed a little pressure put on. Each time we spoke, she would ask, "How is the book going?" Sheri asked with the expectation in her voice that I was indeed following through. No way did I want to let Sheri, Roy, me, or anyone else down. I loved the extra push and inspiration she gave me to help finish my book. I needed it!

Last summer, Sheri and her husband Jon (who had a near death experience right after Sheri's cancer battle) had informed me they were going to be leaving and moving to Colorado. My heart was broken because

I loved having them as neighbors and adored them as friends. Though with everything they had both just endured, I understood the need for a new beginning and a change of pace. Even now that they are both living happily in Colorado, Sheri continues to keep in touch and ask me how my book is coming along. I was thrilled to tell her I was inspired again and agreed to "fight" to finish it rather than easily give up.

So, here I am being vulnerable and opening up my heart and soul. I am giving everyone insight into the many personal struggles I have faced throughout my life so far in the hopes that hearing "you are not alone" will make a significant difference. Knowing others have been there and can understand what you are going through is huge. Simply hearing we have had similar struggles and are not alone helps so much. Reading about or listening to others' hardships actually gave me strength. I can only hope what I am sharing produces a similar, positive outcome for someone else.

Depression and mental illness are real problems that are not disappearing any time soon. Therefore, we need to find a way to minimize the harmful effects caused by them. It won't be easy until people start speaking up and letting society know it's alright to admit you are sad or depressed. It's okay to ask for help and not try to fight it alone. If used in a positive manner, vulnerability can be a strength instead of a weakness. We need to be open to share our disappointments as well as our triumphs. It would be wonderful to get to a place where people could be open about their feelings without the constant worry of being scrutinized or judged. We need to come to an understanding that constant perfection is not a true reality. Mistakes are how we learn to grow. What happened today will be gone tomorrow. I believe change is imminent, and kindness is the key to a successful future.

I don't want to lose any more special individuals due to untreated mental illness. What may have begun as mild to moderate depression can too easily end in suicide. From my prior experience, I can attest to how easily that can happen when you no longer feel hope in life. When the world around you suddenly begins to feel lonely, dark, colorless, or flat, that is the time when you need help the most. Unfortunately, many people don't know how to fight it or get the kind of help they so desperately need.

With the use of technology and social media becoming such an easy target for cyberbullying to take place, many teens have been dealing with extraordinary amounts of depression and suicidal thoughts. Others, sadly, have taken the extra lengths to harm or even worse kill themselves.

My husband Scott is currently an administrator at a middle school who deals with a lot of the discipline problems. I have been privy to some of the social media pictures and abuse since many of my friends with kids at the school show me to alert my husband. I have noticed while Snapchat can be fun for some, it has also been a scary and alarming platform for bullying and threats. Many teens seem to like that one because what they say disappears after a certain amount of time. Some of what adolescents are doing and saying is just evil. It's absolutely disgusting and extremely harmful, and it's not all verbal abuse either. I have witnessed many teens physically threatening others, and a few have even threatened death. We currently live in a scary, unpredictable world. I hope by continuing to share, speak out, and fight back, we can create a positive change soon.

Though I had never personally dealt with social media bullying because it didn't exist when I was younger, I can see the serious effects of it today. Even as an adult at my age, I've witnessed nasty, hateful comments being made to others on various platforms. Once this book gets out to the public, I am sure I will have to deal with that myself. So many people judge, and not everyone feels the same about certain issues. I cannot even begin to tell you the amount of longtime friendships that have been ruined because of opposing opinions being broadcast over social media. It is truly heartbreaking watching what I thought were good friendships fall apart. Things most likely would have gone a different way if they were able to speak in person. It's very sad.

Look at the major divisions in our country right now over politics. I find it extremely upsetting to see humans be so cruel to one another. People don't have to agree, but they should attempt to be respectful of others' opinions. Debates can be great because they raise awareness and allow you to see different sides and perspectives. Unfortunately, they aren't always conducted in a respectful manner. There doesn't seem to be any middle ground. You are either far right or far left, and there is no meeting in the middle on any of the topics. People are losing friends and family members over what should be respectful political discussions. I don't think individuals realize how much harm they are causing with the harsh, often demeaning words they use to make a point. The freedom and use of technology nowadays, while convenient, has also been detrimental. I wish people would be more aware and careful about what they do and say in regard to others. That goes for all encounters we have with people, whether it stems from social media or not.

From anxiety and depression alone, whether it came from social media or elsewhere, I have already endured the tragic loss of too many loved ones. Regrettably, they weren't able to find the help they needed in time to prevent them from taking their own lives. Looking back at what I went through, I can see how easily I could have been one of the statistics. I literally cried for help in my doctor's office the day I felt I could not go on. He unfortunately did not recognize the signs and then help me. Thank goodness I didn't accidently overdose and die. It's plain to see how easily it could happen to someone in the midst of a downfall. If people you care about hit a storm and cannot see beyond the dark clouds, their life could take a turn for the worse and possibly be in jeopardy. It's good to be aware of the signs.

One of the things about suicide that's important to understand is that it isn't always something individuals contemplate for years. It can be a brief moment in time when people can't see beyond the grief or sadness they are experiencing. Sadly, some suicides can be impulsive.

There was a day I vividly remember when I was about 12 years old that I actually contemplated suicide. My parents wouldn't let me go to a Halloween party, while all my other friends were allowed to go. I could not understand why my parents were so adamant about saying no. I was the only one out of my group of friends who wouldn't be there. The anger and rage I was feeling inside over this stupid party consumed me so much that I began thinking about taking a bunch of pills to get back at my parents. I thought, *I'll just kill myself and show them*. It still haunts me how seriously I entertained this utterly disturbing thought.

Young brains can travel down dark roads easily. The smallest things can feel like the biggest problems in the world to them. It was truly idiotic for me to believe taking a bunch of pills (which would've probably ended up with me having my stomach pumped) could've solved my problems. Or worse, what if I had accidently killed myself? I clearly see the consequences now, but I didn't have the tools to realize them then. Sadly, I have no doubt a single fight with someone has triggered a real attempt at suicide. It's truly horrific to think about it that way, but I'm sure it has happened more than once. Someone's loved one could be gone in a flash. That is exactly why this topic is so important. We have to keep talking about it in order to make a difference and create necessary change.

Now that I am through my bout with postpartum depression and have put the past behind me, I can see a brighter future. I have new tools to combat depression. However, during the year or so I was in the middle of it all, I couldn't see my world getting any better or easier. I didn't want to die, but I certainly didn't want to keep living the way I was. It was basically one year of my life. There have been many more years in my lifetime I truly enjoyed. Life is a precious gift. The ups are definitely more fun than the downs, but getting past those tough experiences make us stronger.

Learning to cope with grief, sadness, frustration, and stress is crucial. We are going to continue experiencing those feelings because that is life. To have a good life, proper coping skills and the right tools are essential. It isn't enough to simply say, "just think positive and everything will be okay." When you say those words to individuals who are truly depressed, they are probably thinking about wanting to punch you. It's not that easy. Most people need to build the skills first and learn how to make the positive change in their brains. I have hope we can get to that place by continuing to be open and not be ashamed to talk about mental illness.

I have lost way too many people in my life who have committed suicide. It's probably one of the hardest things to deal with because you always wonder what you could have done to prevent it or save them. Many unanswered questions cause tumultuous grief to those left behind. It is unbelievably difficult to bear when we are unable to answer the "why." I believe the individuals we have lost from suicide could have led impeccable lives if they had been given the tools and had the ability to stick with it, fight, and pull through. But sometimes our dearest loved ones get to the point where they feel there is no way out. In some instances, there may be recognizable signs, while others come as a complete and utter shock. We must keep fighting for better solutions regarding mental health and find ways to help conquer depression before it is too late.

More and more stories are all over the news, magazines, and social media about suicide being on the rise. As far as children and teens are concerned, I strongly feel we are lacking in the mental health department in our schools. I believe we need to hire more counselors to handle the number of students who need mental or behavioral help and guidance. We are taught that early intervention is key for many educational needs. The same philosophy should hold true regarding mental health. Until there are enough experts on hand to meet the needs of students' mental wellness in schools, the problem will undoubtedly remain the same.

Everyone is different in response to finding the right healing modality that works best for him or her. However, I bet if I had a punching bag and gloves in the corner of my classroom and could teach my students how to let out their frustrations on the bag, there would be a positive change in their mental state. With the right training and directions, I could see how it would benefit several kids.

The bottom line is that depression is serious, and we need to find ways to overcome it. Every life matters, and mental health should no longer be treated as taboo. Unfortunately, it's still that way in certain cultures. One of my good friends described how hard it was to watch her mother suffer from depression and not be able to get any help. Mental health was greatly looked down upon in her culture and was not to be spoken about. I hope we see a day when acceptance and change will come for those particular cultures who are suffering.

It isn't only in certain cultures that a negative stigma has surrounded mental illness for decades.

Perhaps the term "mental illness" should be changed to "whole body wellness" since this problem does indeed affect our physical and social/emotional well-being. I doubt one person can say they themselves or someone they're close to has not suffered from mental illness before.

In the past (and still today), I believe society has made it embarrassing and shameful to admit to having depression or problems with mental health. Perhaps many people preferred to hide the fact or deny they struggled with this issue for fear of sounding weak or being judged negatively. From my own perspective, I know there are still people who feel too embarrassed or uncomfortable to seek help. It is a shame it has taken, and is continuing to take, so long to find a positive cure for this illness. I know I sure don't want to lose any more friends or family members because of it. Like my neighbor Sheri, I am willing to "put up my dukes" and fight in order to help change the perception of the negative stigma surrounding mental illness.

Though I think we can agree strides have been made to help people deal with depression, I feel it is our duty to keep talking about it. We must keep pressing this subject so no other incredible human lives are lost. In honor of the many lives we have seen destroyed due to depression and suicide, I want to speak out for the quiet ones. I have shared my own struggles so you don't have to. Yet, if you can become strong enough one day to share your story and hardships with others, I highly recommend you do so. It could possibly save someone's life. If I can save even one life by letting people know they are not alone, not all is lost, and they can fight through this, then I will be deeply gratified.

No doubt I have been knocked down in my life. I am well aware other tragedies will come my way causing more blues and depression. However, when it hits, I now have some tools to eventually get myself out of it. For now, I choose to box the blues away. I'm not saying everyone should do it my way. Instead, I am trying to show you there is another way out. Please don't give up the fight. No matter what has happened in your past, you are a valuable human being, and your life is worth it.

Round 12

TAKING IT ON THE CHIN

I feel it necessary to touch on this subject before the story ends since it has caused one of the biggest states of depression in recent decades. Something colossal and monstrous has happened in our world today I don't think many of us expected or were prepared for. Those who were alive during the 1918 influenza (flu) pandemic might have a bit more understanding of this, but not many of us have ever experienced a worldwide pandemic such as COVID-19, nicknamed the coronavirus. There was nothing any of us could have done about it. We had no other choice but to take it on the chin.

We have never been on a nationwide or state lockdown of such great magnitude. Never have we seen our friends and neighbors walking along the streets or going to get groceries with masks and gloves on. We have never been instructed to stay six feet apart from everyone we might come into contact with. Social distancing certainly was not in my vocabulary prior to the pandemic. Though some of us may like to social distance ourselves and enjoy staying home, we have never been "ordered" to do so by our government before. This is brand new, unfamiliar territory we are having to work out together. I'm acutely aware this pandemic has caused serious depression and suicidal thoughts among many individuals. It has definitely affected me. At times, I felt myself teetering on the edge of moderate to severe depression once more.

This pandemic certainly has created a sense of anxiety and fear among many individuals, including me. We as a society and nation definitely are not used to living under these strict government rules that are limiting our usual freedoms. While I agree with and understand the need to keep everyone safe, it is unheard of to have restaurants, bars, movie theaters, shops, and even schools closed like this. We haven't ever had to deal with those types of extreme shutdowns before. I thought the world would come to an end before I ever thought Disneyland would shut its doors. It's the happiest place on Earth, you know. What will happen to Mickey Mouse, Donald Duck, and Goofy?

What will all the Disney princes and princesses do? I think I might have a slight idea. I bet the amount of babies born in 2021 will be a higher statistical number than ever before. Seriously though, with Disneyland being closed along with everything else we enjoy, where will all the people go to find their new happy place?

Our favorite shows have been postponed. Concerts, theaters, and major sports have been canceled. Our usual expectations of easily being able to go out to attend events, blow off steam, or just simply go somewhere to have fun have been altered in a serious way. With many of our outlets for relieving stress taken away from us, it's no wonder mental health problems are on the rise.

My family certainly felt the effects of the restrictions from COVID-19. My daughter, Macie, is a beautiful singer who also enjoys performing in musicals at a little theater we have in town. She has been bummed out about not getting to see her friends, perform in her dance class, or act in upcoming plays since they have been postponed. In addition, since Macie had just turned 11 this year, we thought it would be the perfect time to take her to see a musical performance in L.A. at the Pantages Theatre for her very first time. We bought her tickets to see *Hamilton* for Christmas and *Mean Girls* for her birthday. Scott and I had never seen our daughter this excited about a present before. She was over the moon with excitement about getting to see the musicals. Unfortunately, they were both canceled.

My husband and I were preparing for days thinking about the best way to break the news to Macie. We were certain the cancelation of the musicals would devastate her. Scott and I were ready for tears and several days of despair, so we came up with what we thought was a really good plan. Scott and I decided to soften the blow by telling Macie we would do our best to try and take her to a Broadway show in New York one day.

As we prepared for the upset and fountain of tears, our daughter surprised us. She said, "It's okay, Mom and Dad. I know some kids don't even get presents at all, and I already feel special enough." Oh my goodness gracious, what 11-year-old child is mature enough to say something like that? I can't take credit for her thoughtful response because I acted like a little baby when my husband told me my surprise birthday present from him (which was going to see Nora Jones at the Greek Theatre) had been canceled now too. It's tough not having fun adventures to look forward to, and it made me feel quite depressed. I definitely did not handle the news as well as my daughter. She has the biggest heart of any little girl I know and is purely beautiful on the inside and out. Macie has an amazing spirit. However, I want to point out it does not mean she doesn't experience her own ups and downs as well. Depression has hit her at times even in her very young age. It has already sunk its claws into both of my children, especially during this pandemic.

In addition to the loss of large events, even our home entertainment has unfortunately been very limited these days. It has been difficult to get our favorite programs on TV since many of them are shot with a live audience or require actors to be in proximity of each other. It has been tough for actors to film since it's nearly impossible for them to abide by the social distancing rules, so our choice of programs has been dwindling. Instead, we have mainly been limited to older shows, documentaries, and movies that were made before the coronavirus hit us.

One of, if not the biggest entertainment phenomenon of this year (released in March of 2020) has got to be the bizarre and insane story about a zookeeper named Joe Exotic. The documentary was called *Tiger King: Murder, Mayhem and Madness.* It seriously was the craziest series I have ever watched. As I am writing this in the summer of 2020, it is still creating a huge amount of buzz all over the world. There is plenty to explore where that whole tale and mystery is concerned, I am sure. Before my book is finished, I have to wonder if they will have solved the murder of Carol Baskin's husband. Did Carol's tiger get a tasty human snack or was it another dark, mysterious secret event that took place? Hopefully one day that mystery will be solved. If you haven't heard of the *Tiger King*, then you haven't lived through COVID-19. There wasn't much else to do other than binge-watch the hell out of that show as many people did. While I'm sure a movie made about it will pull in all kinds of viewers, I don't think it could even compare to the raw insanity of its characters in real life.

Similar to *Tiger King* was another popular, yet disturbing, documentary I watched called *The Jinx*. It had to do with a crime involving a member of one of the richest families in New York. It was a story about Robert Durst and murder. This docuseries came out in 2015, but Robert Durst's trial has yet to begin. It is supposed to be coming up soon once courts can reopen safely from the virus. Prior to directing *The Jinx*, Andrew Jarecki had also directed a film called *All Good Things,* which included actors Ryan Gosling and Kirsten Dunst. The film was inspired by Robert Durst's strange life where he had originally been accused of murdering his wife. If you watch either of these films, you will get an interesting view of what serious mental illness looks like. It's no joke. *The Jinx* added a whole new element to the bizarre life of Robert Durst, as he is now being accused of two more killings in addition to his wife's murder. It was a nail-biting, suspenseful series to watch. However, unlike *Tiger King*, the mystery was undeniably solved on film. Yet, as it stands in real time today, we still do not know the outcome of Robert Durst's future. We will have to wait for the jury to determine his fate.

Those were two of the strangest, most suspenseful, and mysterious documentaries I have ever seen. What watching those shows did for me was help me realize that what we are all going through during this time of COVID-19 is not as bad as some. While this may be another depressing time in life, I am pleased to know that while I might be going crazy at times, I am definitely not as batshit crazy as the main characters in those documentaries. Neither are many of you, so I just put a positive spin on it for all of you. Though, sadly, I feel if either Joe Exotic or Robert Durst would have been able to get some help or an intervention early on for their apparent mental illness, perhaps they wouldn't have committed such heinous crimes. Too bad I couldn't have shown them my boxing routine. As for now, I can only hope justice is served and they learn and grow from their mistakes and wrongdoings.

Speaking of justice, it actually prevailed recently regarding a cult leader who was sentenced to life in prison. This was another documentary series I watched during COVID called *The Vow*. It was marginally about wealthy people and celebrities who believed they were joining a self-improvement group called NXIVM. Keith

Raniere was their leader. The series showed members of NXIVM slowly beginning to realize things were not as they seemed and started planning their escape.

An extremely concerned mother and famous actress, Catherine Oxenberg from the 90's soap opera *Dynasty*, went to great lengths to save her daughter India from the evil happenings of the cult. After a long and tedious battle, Catherine's daughter finally got out. India is quoted in *People* magazine's October 26, 2020 issue referring to her mom by saying, "Sometimes I'd have a panic attack, and she would just hold me and tell me I was safe." In referencing the years after she escaped NXIVM, the article also stated, "In the two years since, India has regained her strength both inside and out thanks to therapy—and regular boxing workouts."

Let me repeat that: A beautiful girl, who was branded with Keith Reniere's initials and nearly destroyed by this awful man and his cult, chose boxing as her healing strategy. The article insinuates India is learning, healing, and becoming stronger. As you can see, boxing is a powerful tool for mental distress and more.

Though the rest of us are free and not in prison right now like the men in those documentaries, we can similarly relate to feeling locked up during this crazy pandemic. While I'm certain the isolation we are experiencing from COVID-19 can't truly compare to the reality of living within the confining walls of a jail cell, it can still play tricks on our minds. For me, there have been moments where I have felt claustrophobic within the confines of my own home. I can also attest to many others feeling the same way since my friends have expressed feeling like prisoners at times during quarantine. Personally, I get antsy and impatient being in the same place all the time. I have most definitely experienced cabin fever. The places we usually go to escape or get some fresh air have been rather limited. Our normal way of living, as well as our livelihood, has been uprooted rather severely. While we are already dealing with the hardships of our favorite activities being canceled or postponed, we are also having to endure other means of recreational outlets being shut down.

Among other places my family loved to go, we have now been blocked from certain hiking trails, beaches, and parks. In addition to my own family, I know many others have been struggling to find the best way to handle this new normal. While several parents struggle to keep their own sanity intact, they are currently having to find other activities for their children to do, which don't include their usual exercise or social routines. Plus, in addition to working (if they still have a job), parents are having to not only find ways to keep their children entertained, but they have to homeschool them now as well.

While I am a public-school teacher myself preparing lessons for virtual learning and offering curriculum to my elementary class, I have found it rather difficult to homeschool my own children. I am not going to lie—teaching my own kids has been an absolute nightmare at times. Homeschooling is not fun, I'm sorry to say. I truly feel for the parents who are having to take this extra job on themselves in addition to their normal working schedules. Beyond managing to figure out the technical issues, they also have to find a way to help teach the classwork that may not be familiar to their kids. I can certainly tell you from trying to help my kids with their schoolwork, I embarrassingly found out I am *not* smarter than a fifth grader.

With the reopening of school drawing near, people are fretting about the decision to send kids back to campus with safety precautions or have them continue to do virtual learning from home. There have been so many ugly arguments over it. Sadly, I see people losing friends over their strong divisions in opinions about what is best for our children as well as from politics that have a strong hand in it all. As a parent and a teacher, I can understand both sides of the argument. Of course, we want our kids to go back to school like normal. We want our whole world to be normal again, but it isn't. It won't be until we get a handle on this virus.

While their physical health is in danger from COVID-19, our children's mental health is at stake as well. We know proper health is a combination of physical and mental well-being. One doesn't work without the other. Being a mom of a son who is high risk where the coronavirus is concerned, I have to weigh all my options and take it seriously. This is a narrow road to travel right now. None of the decisions we make are easy. The last thing I want to do is to have to homeschool my children again. However, many of us don't have a choice and will have to suck it up a bit longer until the virus runs its course. It's awful, I know. It has made several of us want to drink more.

I completely understand people struggling with alcohol dependency during this time. While I have never been a big drinker, I can definitely admit to having a few more gin and tonics than usual after trying to do schoolwork at home with my children. When my kids brought up that they noticed I was having a couple more alcoholic beverages than usual, I wanted to say, "No shit, I am having to drink more. Alcohol is the only way I can help you wonderful, precious, little boogers when you are whining about your distance learning. I still love you though." (By the way, during COVID-19, I actually called it "sanity juice" instead of alcohol.) With all joking aside, it is true people are turning to alcohol because of the stress and depression the pandemic has caused. This is why it is so important for our nation to get a handle on mental health. I believe it has become more important now than ever before.

Without normal schooling for our children, creating some type of structure and routines at home has been a chore in itself. While I have never been a morning person and absolutely dreaded waking up early to get the kids and me ready for school, at least it provided a solid structure for the day. Since I started working from home, I have struggled to keep track of time, the date, when to eat, when to shower, or even get dressed. Some days I didn't even bother. Yes, I am aware that's kind of disgusting, but I very much know I am not the only one.

As a teacher, I was pretty good at creating schedules and working with strict timeframes. During this pandemic, I have not been able to keep myself on track. I have felt lost and confused most days. My job has become ten times as difficult since I am having to learn a brand-new way of teaching online. Personally, I have been putting in 12 to 14-hour days and not eating at all until about 7:00 p.m. I have barely been able to say hello to my own kids, let alone try to help them navigate their schoolwork.

Both of my children have been very depressed during this pandemic. While I try my best to comfort them and explain this is something new we are all having to face, it doesn't really help change their feelings of sadness and isolation. Both of my kids have been tearing up saying they hate online learning and are dying to go back to school with their friends and teachers. Every person in my family has experienced emotional and depressing times throughout this coronavirus ordeal. Most of my friends have admitted to feeling depressed more than usual as well. Who are we kidding? Everyone has to be feeling it one way or another as the pandemic has affected not only us but the entire world.

Beyond trying to manage and find some sort of structure for our children, there is another problem many of us parents have been troubleshooting. As if it wasn't already a major issue, due to the coronavirus, our kids have been staring at screens and actually having to employ more electronic devices than they were using before. Prior to the pandemic, my husband and I had to battle our children over the use of their electronic toys and games. Now they are on electronics constantly just from the schoolwork they are being given. Both of them talk about their eyes and head hurting from too much screen time. I'm sure a lot of parents are still allowing their children to use iPads, iPhones, play video games and such just to get a much-needed break. I get it, believe me. However, their poor little brains have got to be on electronic overload. I could be wrong, but I feel like I've seen extra emotional distraught and depression caused by too much electronic time. Unfortunately, we have limited options right now.

My own kids, in addition to many of my friends' kids, are having a difficult time adjusting to the changes put in place because of COVID-19. They are having more emotional battles and depressive episodes than I have ever seen. When you're a kid or a teen, your life revolves around friends. Now many of them have not seen their friends in months. Kids who used to whine about having to go to school are now begging to go back. They aren't accustomed to this kind of lifestyle, nor are we as adults. It's tough to be living in a free country that isn't very free at the moment. While I completely understand the need to keep everyone safe, I find it difficult to wear a mask for long periods of time. It's hard to wear a mask while out walking your dog or trying to exercise. While I get the necessity of masks and wear them out of respect for others, I still find them to be pretty darn uncomfortable.

Beyond having to wear masks, there have been several other inconveniences we have had to experience on different levels as well. When I last got my hair colored and cut, I didn't think it would actually be the "last" time I would be getting it done. It's hilarious how many of us have had to find alternative ways to cover up our roots. Well, maybe "hilarious" isn't quite the right word for it. It was actually a bit devastating and slightly shocking to see so much gray in my hair. I guess I didn't realize how much gray hair I had since I kept it colored on a regular basis. I can't even begin to comprehend what some of the ladies are doing about their manicures and pedicures, facials, Botox, lip injections, and such. I would never consider myself a vain person, but I might just have to join the party after this virus is gone. In fact, just go ahead and sign me up for all of that and more. I think I'm going to need it by the time this pandemic finally ends.

For men, it's kind of funny how mohawks and buzz cuts have started to trend again. I have even seen mullets making a comeback, although Joe Exotic will probably have to get the credit for that one. Some of us have simply had to let go of any vanity for the time being. What I have loved and gotten a kick out of recently was seeing families attempt to cut each other's hair. It has been adorable watching spouses trying to trim each other's locks. I've also enjoyed witnessing some of the kids attempting to cut their parent's hair. Those are some brave adults right there. Thanks, but I'm good with my messy hair and gray roots. I've learned to do a killer ponytail and found a great hair color spray. I can wait it out.

Like me, I know a lot of women who have been going without makeup or fixing their hair most days. In addition, sweatpants and pajamas have become the new everyday fashion. One day, I decided I would attempt my usual makeup and hair routine only to find out I didn't have a clue how to make it look decent anymore. It had been so long. I seriously felt like a teenager trying to put color on my face for the first time. Where does the eyeliner go? How do I put eyeshadow on properly? Oh, you're supposed to use a primer? Who remembers? It seriously wasn't pretty. Those are some of the sillier things we have had to bear with while waiting for the stay-at-home orders to be lifted.

While we may have whined and complained about them, those tended to be some of the easier problems this nasty virus has caused. All joking aside, people have suffered unbearably, and many individual's health has been affected by COVID-19. Countless people have lost their loved ones. Several individuals lost their jobs, could not afford to pay their mortgages or rent, let alone provide enough food for their families. Some parents have also been struggling to find daycare for their children who are not able to go to school since many of them are not open yet. How can these parents keep their jobs and go to work with small children at home? These are serious issues and tragedies people have been experiencing from the virus.

In addition, who in their right minds ever thought we would have a shortage of toilet paper? It has been absurd watching people stand in long lines, running and fighting to get toilet paper, paper towels, napkins, tissue, baby wipes, and anything else they can use to clean up their personal business with. Seriously, when in your life have you ever thought, Hmm, I wonder what I am going to use to wipe my butt with tomorrow? You even see people taking pictures with rolls of toilet paper as if they won the lottery. It is actually making me rethink trimming my trees. You never know when those extra leaves might come in handy. It's uncanny, yet it's all real.

What has also become a reality has been virtual or drive-by birthday celebrations and special events. What the hell? Did you ever think you would be driving in a car holding up a special sign for your grandparents while they smile and wave to you from their front door or garage? Insane, right? These meaningful occasions are all having to take a back seat to this crazy virus.

Teachers were driving by their students' neighborhoods while families stood outside and waved. It seemed like such a sweet, caring thing to do. Then they were told that was a big no-no due to the stay-at-home order. Humans as a whole are extremely social beings, so having to quarantine has been like torture for some.

People who desperately miss their families have been forced to visit over the internet. There's no other choice if you want to stay safe. In addition, business meetings and social events have been conducted over Skype, Zoom, Houseparty, and other social media platforms. Personally, I don't think I can handle any more Zoom meetings. I know many of my friends and coworkers are feeling the exact same way. We are ready to throw Zoom meetings in the crapper (a dirty, smelly, disgusting one even). Seriously, staring at a bunch of different people in squares on a tiny screen gets to be brutal after a while.

If you are a Gen Xer like me, or older, then you have to remember watching *The Brady Bunch* on TV. Who didn't love *The Brady Bunch?* Prior to all of this technology and the reoccurring Zoom meetings, I thought the introduction to that show was the coolest thing ever. I had never seen anyone looking at each other in little squares like that before. The family appeared to be incredibly happy as they smiled so sweetly and looked all around at each other. There is no way possible they could have been happy looking at each other in those tiny boxes. Watch it again and study all their fake smiles. You'll see!

Whenever my Zoom screen comes on, I just want to take out my boxing gloves and punch the daylights out of those four sides and corners because they make me crazy. Not the people though. It's the people who I adore and do not want to punch, just the squares they are in. I am tired of looking at screens to see my friends, coworkers, students, and others I miss. I want to see them in real life and hug them to pieces. Like most everyone else, I am so completely over this coronavirus crap. I wish I could just box the hell out of it right now.

What's immensely tough is the virus is prohibiting us from real social interactions as we knew them. We can't hug or shake hands with people anymore. It is not only instinct but socially appropriate to hold out your hand when meeting someone new. Instead, we are doing the awkward elbow bump and things like that to make do. It's weird. I have to wonder if the typical handshake greeting will forever be changed after this.

More importantly, human touch can be such a valuable commodity when it comes to health and wellness. I know this type of isolation has caused suffering for certain people who are not used to being alone. My kids ask for hugs every day just to maintain a little bit of personal contact. They are devastated they haven't been able to hang out with a group of friends. Talking to them on screens doesn't quite do the trick. There is no denying the unimaginable amount of loss, sadness, anxiety, fear, depression, and tragedy this worldwide pandemic has caused.

I feel for the children and individuals who are having to endure more abuse at home. I'm aware that more people are turning to alcohol and drugs to escape this extra hardship they are facing while being quarantined. I for one am certainly not innocent. Unfortunately, that was how I started handling my stress when first becoming deeply depressed over all of this. Stupidly, I hadn't started my boxing routine again, which has always helped when I've gotten into a slump. One thing I have going for me is that my husband and I don't really fight. I imagine the divorce rate has reached new heights from the stress and having to be in close quarters. While there are so many uncertainties and anxieties we are facing, it is also important to be grateful and try to remember the good in things each day.

I could go on and on about all the misfortunes and absurdities the COVID-19 disaster has created. However, there are positive aspects to remember as well. It's important to find gratitude in times of uncertainty and despair to deter depression. One beautiful example is families spending more time with each other. Another is certain people who tend to be a little more uptight or anxious have been forced to relax and take things slower. Traffic has been lighter. That's a huge ordeal if you live in big cities like New York, Chicago, or Los Angeles. It's been years since I have been able to drive the normal speed limit on a California freeway without having to break or stop every couple of miles. For people who really are stuck at home and are not able to drive and see the outside world, many of those individuals have been focusing on art, music, or other hobbies which can be an uplifting escape. For certain individuals who don't like crowds, they are probably quite content with the demands of social distancing which may be giving them their much-needed personal space (that would be me).

Wouldn't it be wonderful if crowded places, such as Disneyland for an example, enforced the lines with tape or floor signs like the grocery stores have been doing? Then you wouldn't have to feel the person behind you bumping and rubbing all over you, breathing down your neck, sweating on you, or stinking with their yucky body odor. Not that I'm speaking from experience (I totally am), but I find it annoying when people do not honor personal space.

Perhaps some good things could come out of this massive devastation after all. It's good to stop and smell the roses once in a while during these trying times. I'm not trying to make light of COVID-19 because it has truly caused a major disturbance. I just think to train our brains to be more positive, we have to find some aspect of goodness in even the worst situations.

There is a valid point I would like to make by mentioning all of the good things, as well as hardships we are enduring, as we wade through these murky, unclear waters together. "Stronger together" and "we are all in this together" have been a couple of the main mottos during these difficult times. At least some people are trying to be stronger and more united as a whole. We hear endless, heartwarming stories of good deeds and those helping to make a difference. We have to work together and be more united beyond just the "Rona" (another nickname for Covid-19) crisis. Tragically, our nation has been divided not from the virus alone, but from politics, racism, sexual preference, and religion. We are all humans trying to navigate this world together, and the massive separation between us cannot be beneficial for anyone. We have to find a way for peace, love, and kindness to prevail.

I completely understand the ton of extra stress and uncertainty as we maneuver through each day and week wondering what is to come in the near future. We don't know yet what the future holds. Unfortunately, when things are uncertain, chaotic, or stressful is when mental illness tends to rear its ugly head. No doubt battles with depression will be on the rise. I have not spoken to a single friend or family member who hasn't felt some form of the blues while enduring this pandemic. I know I have already experienced my own fair share of ups and downs. It's common in times like these.

Though I wish I could tell you otherwise, I'm finding this pandemic has messed with my physical and mental emotions quite thoroughly. While the exhaustion from my job and homelife trying to take care of so many kids could be extremely draining at times, the mental taxation from the coronavirus has been affecting me on a very different level. While I hadn't been getting the same amount of exercise or finding healthy ways to blow off steam initially, my whole system and body began to feel the effects. Before things got too out of control, I thought about what I had learned from Roy again. I put my skills, knowledge, and prior training back into action. Now I am happy to say I have been fighting through it all and boxing my ass off. (I'd box my thighs or muffin top off if I could, but unfortunately it doesn't seem to work that way for me.) I'm just thrilled to have found an outlet that works. Boxing has been the best healing device I know for conquering depression.

It took some time, but I began to get pumped and ready to fight instead of allowing the depression over all this to overtake me. I didn't want to just sit there and take it on the chin. I did have to at first because there was nothing I could do about the coronavirus, but I didn't want to. So, I decided I would get ready to rumble instead. Who didn't love listening to Michael Buffer yell, "Let's get ready to rumble!" before the start of the fights? It is one of the most well-known, classic phrases of all time. That was pure genius on his part. Oh, what I would give to be able to go to an event and hear his voice in person right now.

Due to the depression I was feeling over this pandemic, I can honestly say I have not trained this hard in boxing since my bout with postpartum depression over ten years ago. The one difference is I haven't felt the necessity to rely on a professional boxer as much as I did the first time around. What I learned from Roy Jones Jr. provided me with enough skills and knowhow to get out of a dark place if I began to go there again. Remembering those skills and putting them back into action has helped me tremendously. Thankfully, I learned how to fight my mental battles and am stronger because of it.

Throughout this whole process, I have made enormous strides in learning how to conquer my depression and blues when they have tried to beat me down. For many years, I was pessimistic and looked at the glass as being half empty. With the help of Roy and other various individuals in my life who have inspired me, I can now say I typically see the glass as being more than half full. Looking at the bright side is a much happier and fulfilling way to live my life. I have learned how to let go of any ego and be my authentic self who is sensitive, kind, and caring (with a sassy, fiery, potty mouth at times). Though I do try my best, nobody is perfect. I really focus on trying to learn from past mistakes and attempt to be a better person every day.

How bizarre that I didn't even remotely like boxing at all to begin with, and yet the sport has made one of the biggest impacts on my life. There are numerous boxing metaphors which really sum things up for me. When I had postpartum depression, I had given up and was ready to throw in the towel. I have definitely been boxed into a corner, sucker-punched, and taken off guard many times. I have learned from those instances though, and I refuse to put up with any more low blows from people. I can choose who I accept in my life and stay away from people who try to bring me down. If someone does try to knock me out, I won't stay down for the count. From here on out, I promise to get back up and keep fighting.

In the past I may have taken it on the chin from people, but I won't be doing it anymore. I plan to keep my guard up and block anything negative attempting to come my way. When I was depressed, life felt like my biggest opponent. However, I have come to realize I am my own opponent. It's up to me to make the choices. I can decide whether or not to step into the ring, bob and weave, or come out swinging. At this point in my life, I am trying to be my best self by putting in the effort to go the distance. From this point forward, I want to fight for what is good and right.

As I write this in the midst of the pandemic during 2020, it is unclear what we will be facing in the months and years to come as COVID-19 is not cured or finished affecting us yet. Though the virus has made it feel like the movie *Groundhog Day* all over again as we live in quarantine, uncertain of its ending or demise, we can't allow it to defeat us. Do not give into this virus like Phil Connors was going to do with his unlucky circumstances and let it "be cold, gray, and last you for the rest of your life." You can choose to come out swinging and throw the next punch instead.

While nobody likes it, this will not be the only virus or difficult situation we will ever have to overcome, but we will certainly make it through. We have to expect more trials and tribulations during our lives while we experience ups and downs forever. There's a reason people say life is like a roller coaster. Try to keep things in perspective as there will be many more hills to climb, hurtles to jump over, deep waters to swim through, and other obstacles heading our way. Think of it as a challenge instead of a curse. Life is a gift, but it's not always easy or perfect. However, I believe you can fight through anything that bothers you and keep hope alive. You just have to find the right way.

Always keep in mind you are special just the way you are, you are valuable and unique, there are people who care about you, and most of all—your life matters. Keep doing what you are doing to stay afloat. If you ever find yourself at a loss and don't know what to do, please join with me and say, I am "willing" to begin boxing the blues away.

Acknowledgments

First and foremost, I would like to extend a sincere thank-you to my buddy Greg and Roy Jones Jr., as this book would never have been made possible without them. Greg has remained a close family friend of mine for as long as I can remember. He has been a good listener, helpful mentor, and all-around wonderful friend. I will always cherish the fun times our families had at the Newport Beach House as well as all the eggnog parties. I had the best times hanging out with Greg in Manhattan Beach with our friends from the Kings hockey team and other great friends we had made from Harry O's. I will always treasure the memories and times hanging out with him and Roy. Though Greg now lives in another state, I am thrilled we have continued to remain close. I cannot thank Greg enough for his friendship, listening ear, and advice over the years. Besides always looking out for me and my friends, I am also very grateful to him for inviting me over to meet Roy. Who knew it would have made the enormous impact it has? Greg, you are not only a great friend but a truly amazing human being. Thank you for always being "the real McCoy."

Next, I owe a lot to Roy Jones Jr. While he was a ton of fun to hang out with in my younger years, he made a bigger difference in my life as I got older. For him to take time away from his own busy schedule and life to help me was pure generosity. I cannot thank him enough for providing me with the tools, inspiration, and encouragement I needed to be able to find the confidence and willpower to be a true fighter. Roy taught me incredible skills that have benefited my health and life in more ways than he will ever know. Roy is not only a friend but is also a hero to me. He literally helped save my life. I wholeheartedly want to thank Roy and his entire family for allowing him to be a part of this crazy adventure with me.

My husband Scott has my heart and soul. He is my rock who stayed with me and helped me get through The Dark Times. He is an amazing partner who has supported me during tough moments and has continued to love me for who I am. He allows me to truly be myself. I could never have made it to where I am without his continued love and support. He is my everything. Scott, thank you for choosing me to spend your life with.

Maverick and Macie are the most compassionate, talented, warm-hearted, generous kids I could ever have hoped for. They bring so much joy and happiness to my life every day. Though I battled through those tough times early on, I could not imagine my life without them. They have the most amazing spirits and love for everyone. They are well-mannered and unbelievably well-behaved children. Though Scott and I try our best to corrupt them at times, we don't get very far. I love my kids more than life itself, and I am truly proud and grateful to be their mother. I also owe them a huge thank-you for allowing me the time to work on my book. I love you, Maverick and Macie Jayne.

There aren't even enough words to begin to thank my mom and dad for everything they have done and given me so far in my life. They are incredible role models. My mother especially has been there every step of the way whenever I have needed support, love, or just a shoulder to cry on. She is truly an angel in disguise. My mom and dad are absolutely the best parents and grandparents in the world. Thank you, Mom and Dad, for everything and more. I love you. Dad, I'm so happy you rocked your recent cancer battle and made it through like a champ in order to keep sharing your family's secrets and Italian Mafia stories with me (wink).

I would like to thank Kara, as she has been there for me not only as a sister but also a friend and confidant. There are so many things I have trusted and relied on her for. My sister is one of the kindest, most caring, and helpful individuals I know. I feel very fortunate to have such an amazing sister in my life. Good job marrying Paul as well. Love you, Paul. Thanks for always keeping things light and humorous.

To my twin brothers, Mark and Doug, thank you for being a fun and always entertaining part of my life as adults. I wouldn't choose any other brothers to have in my life. I'm super proud of your accomplishments and love you both very much.

Kathy, you are a wonderful sister-in-law and a talented artist. Thank you so much for working with me to design the cover of the book and more. I am in awe of your incredible skills.

Missy, I'm so happy to have you as a sister-in-law. You are a strong, inspiring woman. Keep kicking ass and putting those bad guys away for us.

Carol, thank you for encouraging me to become a teacher but, more importantly, for helping to find and hire my incredibly handsome and remarkable husband.

Thank you to my wonderful friends Cindy and Cheryl, who I had some of the best times and most memorable experiences with. I appreciate you allowing me to share a little about our stories in this book. I love you both and will forever treasure our friendship.

Meghan, you know I absolutely adore you and your family. It's been amazing to share our stories about our incredible experiences with "Dr. Doogie." I truly value your friendship and I hope our kids' connections remain just as strong throughout their lives.

Thank you to my fearless champion and awesome student and his wonderful family who have endured more than anyone should have to. Thank you for trusting me and allowing me to teach your son. To my amazing student, please remember you are brave, you are smart, you are who you were meant to be, and you are loved for being you.

Ashley and Josh Grant, thank you for being kind, caring, and generous. Thank you for making my student's day and bringing the biggest smile to his face in a time of need.

For my superwomen breast cancer sisters Adrianna and Sheri (plus Cindy and Cheryl, who are also survivors), thank you for your love, support, and encouragement. You are strong warriors! One of these days I hope they will have found a cure or an easier way to kick cancer's butt.

Mama Dee, you are the best caregiver I could have ever hoped for. Thank you so much for loving Maverick (and Macie) as much as you did and do. You are one hell of an amazing woman and grandma.

A ginormous thank you goes out to my sweet Dr. Berberich for your kindness and willingness to take me on as a patient (even though I was such a huge pain in the butt with more than just a hard pregnancy to overcome). It's a bummer you didn't agree to my $100 bet, but you helped save my little miracle baby, Macie

Jayne. Not only were you there to help me with Macie, but you continued to be an enormous support to me several years after. You are absolutely one of the best, most caring doctors I have ever had. I am humbled and grateful to have been your "favorite" patient. Thank you for what you did for me as well as for all the many patients you have helped throughout the years.

In addition to Dr. Berberich, I must also thank my special doctor, "Doogie Howser," plain and simply for being so *f-cking rad*, a brilliant surgeon, and for taking such great care of me.

To Carl Burak (who I feel so incredibly lucky to have been able to connect with those ten-plus years ago), thank you profusely for all of the talks and guidance you have given me along the way. You are an amazing doctor, author, advocate, and friend. I am so grateful that I was blessed with the opportunity to get to know you. You are a caring, generous, one-of-a-kind, incredible human being.

To my editor Deborrah Hoag, you are a remarkable woman who was definitely worth the wait. I love your positive energy and kind spirit. You treated my very personal story with the type of care and sensitivity I needed. It was so much fun spending time talking to you and finding out how much we have in common. I will forever be thankful for your help and expertise. I'm looking forward to our new life-long friendship and hopefully working on more books with you.

Last, I want to thank all the people in my life who have stood by me, provided support, help, or just a genuine smile. You are all remarkable people and have made a world of difference to me and others who you infect with your amazing hearts and genuine gifts of love and greatness. I'm sending hugs, love, peace, and laughter to all of you.

Made in the USA
Las Vegas, NV
28 December 2020

14897511R00138